Connecting Readi...
Grades 7–8

Introduction..2
Features...3
Correlation Chart.................................5
Fluency Checklist.................................6
Progress Record...................................7

🌐 Lesson 1: How Do I Look?
Connecting Background 8
Making Inferences Graphic Organizer.........9
How's the Weather Up There? 10
Brace Face 12
Weird Wardrobe 14

🌐 Lesson 2: Adventurers All
Connecting Background 16
Building Background Graphic Organizer 17
Guard Duty 18
Thanksgiving Then and Now 20
Samoset, Squanto, and Massasoit 22

⚛ Lesson 3: Stargazing
Connecting Background 24
Visualizing Graphic Organizer..................25
Once in a Blue Moon 26
Why Do Stars Twinkle? 28
The Making of a Legend 30

🌐 Lesson 4: Radio Days
Connecting Background 32
Word Meaning Map 33
Careers in Radio 34
Radio to the Rescue 36
From Wired to Wireless 38

⚛ Lesson 5: You Are What You Eat
Connecting Background 40
Summarizing Notes 41
Diets: The Good and the Bad 42
Get Off the Couch! 44
Your New Food Guide 46

⚛ Lesson 6: Eye Witness
Connecting Background 48
Main Idea and Supporting Details
   Graphic Organizer 49
Caring for the Eyes 50
Braille 52
Diseases of the Eye 54

⚛ Lesson 7: A Look Inside
Connecting Background 56
Flowchart 57
The Circulatory System 58
The Digestive System 60
The Nervous System 62

⚛ Lesson 8: Science to the Rescue
Connecting Background 64
Asking Questions Chart............................65
Mosquito Bites 66
Smallpox 68
Measles 70

🌐 Lesson 9: The Simple Life
Connecting Background 72
Text Connections Graphic Organizer.........73
Consumer Culture 74
Don't Watch . . . Live! 76
Henry David Thoreau 78

⚛ Lesson 10: Technology for Living
Connecting Background 80
Problem and Solution Charts 81
Who's Calling? 82
Dots, Dots, and More Dots 84
Exciting News 86

⚛ Lesson 11: Save Us from Ourselves!
Connecting Background 88
Cause and Effect Charts 89
Water for Thought 90
Huge and Growing 92
What's in Your Breath? 94

🌐 Lesson 12: How Great Is Art!
Connecting Background 96
Summarizing Notes 97
Public Murals 98
Anime 100
The Political Cartoon 102

🌐 Lesson 13: Cityscapes
Connecting Background 104
Making Inferences Graphic Organizer.....105
At the Water's Edge 106
The Paris of the South 108
The City Different 110

🌐 Lesson 14: Pursuit of Peace
Connecting Background 112
Monitoring Comprehension Chart 113
Nobel Peace Prize 114
Jody Williams and the ICBL 116
Doctors Without Borders 118

⚛ Lesson 15: Spectacular Science
Connecting Background 120
Sequence Chain 121
Daniel Hale Williams 122
Gertrude B. Elion 124
Ben Carson 126

Answer Key 128

Connecting Reading 7–8, SV 9781419036453

Introduction

Connecting Reading is a program that provides engaging fluency instruction for all of your readers. Students at different reading levels:

- Practice reading selections relating to the same topic.
- Pursue the same instructional goals.
- Interact and build fluency together.

Each lesson focuses on an interesting science or social studies topic. The three articles in each lesson have different reading levels as measured by the Flesch-Kincaid readability scale. Each student reads the selection most appropriate for him or her. Then students discuss the content of their articles. This mixed-ability grouping can promote meaningful interaction so that students build skills in a rich environment of peer-to-peer modeling, discussion, and feedback.

In addition, each passage includes the word count of each line. This provides an easy way to conduct timed readings with your students to assess reading speed.

Components

The following components are resources for the teacher.

- The **Correlation Chart** on page 5 is an easy reference that shows the reading skills, fluency skills, social studies standards, and science standards for each lesson.
- The **Fluency Checklist** on page 6 is a chart that students or teachers use to rate a reader's fluency performance, including word accuracy, rate, use of expression, and phrasing.
- The **Progress Record** is a timed assessment that calculates a student's reading rate. Given by the teacher, it can be used to determine a student's improvement during the year. You may wish to administer the assessment to different students each week.

The following components are part of each lesson.

- **Connecting Background** is a teacher resource that explains the focus skills in each lesson. It identifies the titles and levels of the three selections. The **Theme Notes** section explains how the articles are related and can be read aloud to students prior to beginning the lesson. The **Fluency Focus** explains the fluency skill students will work on, and a quick **Fluency Practice** can

be completed with the group to introduce the skill. The **Comprehension Focus** provides students with an opportunity to practice a reading skill using a nonfiction topic. Even though students are reading different articles, they all practice the same comprehension skill. Finally, a **vocabulary** list targets three words in each article that students may find challenging, either in pronunciation or contextual understanding.

- Each lesson also includes a **graphic organizer** to reinforce the comprehension skill.
- The **three articles** are short and interesting. The articles are leveled for different reading abilities. Students should read the selection that provides a slight challenge but still assures a successful reading experience. A **Fluency Tip** at the bottom of the page guides readers to a specific part of the text where they can practice the lesson's fluency skill.
- A **comprehension assessment** follows each article. Four multiple-choice questions check students' understanding. A fifth, inferential question requires students to respond in complete sentences.

Features

Science or Social Studies Icon
Denotes a science connection (atom) or a social studies connection (world)

Theme Notes
Provides background information to introduce the topic of the selections to students

Vocabulary
Identifies challenging words in each selection

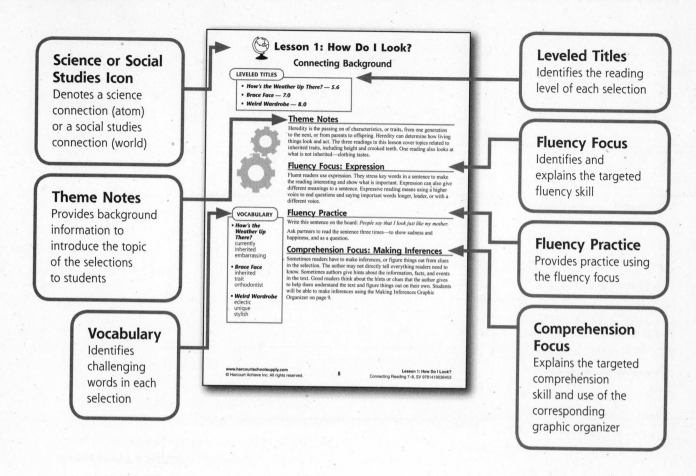

Lesson 1: How Do I Look?
Connecting Background

LEVELED TITLES
- *How's the Weather Up There?* — 5.6
- *Brace Face* — 7.0
- *Weird Wardrobe* — 8.0

Theme Notes
Heredity is the passing on of characteristics, or traits, from one generation to the next, or from parents to offspring. Heredity can determine how living things look and act. The three readings in this lesson cover topics related to inherited traits, including height and crooked teeth. One reading also looks at what is not inherited—clothing tastes.

Fluency Focus: Expression
Fluent readers use expression. They stress key words in a sentence to make the reading interesting and show what is important. Expression can also give different meanings to a sentence. Expressive reading means using a higher voice to end questions and saying important words longer, louder, or with a different voice.

Fluency Practice
Write this sentence on the board: *People say that I look just like my mother.*
Ask partners to read the sentence three times—to show sadness and happiness, and as a question.

Comprehension Focus: Making Inferences
Sometimes readers have to make inferences, or figure things out from clues in the selection. The author may not directly tell everything readers need to know. Sometimes authors give hints about the information, facts, and events in the text. Good readers think about the hints or clues that the author gives to help them understand the text and figure things out on their own. Students will be able to make inferences using the Making Inferences Graphic Organizer on page 9.

VOCABULARY
- *How's the Weather Up There?*
  currently
  inherited
  embarrassing
- *Brace Face*
  inherited
  trait
  orthodontist
- *Weird Wardrobe*
  eclectic
  unique
  stylish

Leveled Titles
Identifies the reading level of each selection

Fluency Focus
Identifies and explains the targeted fluency skill

Fluency Practice
Provides practice using the fluency focus

Comprehension Focus
Explains the targeted comprehension skill and use of the corresponding graphic organizer

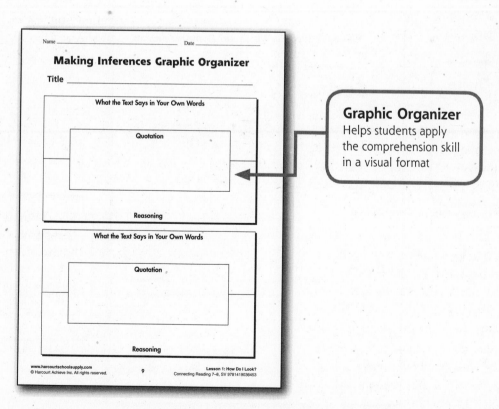

Name _____ Date _____

Making Inferences Graphic Organizer

Title _____

What the Text Says in Your Own Words

Quotation

Reasoning

What the Text Says in Your Own Words

Quotation

Reasoning

www.harcourtschoolsupply.com
© Harcourt Achieve Inc. All rights reserved.
9
Lesson 1: How Do I Look?
Connecting Reading 7–8, SV 9781419036453

Graphic Organizer
Helps students apply the comprehension skill in a visual format

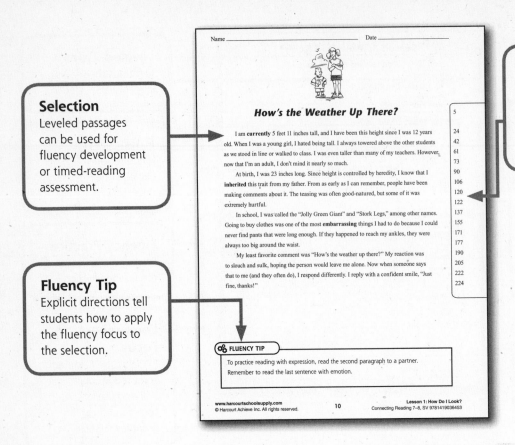

Selection
Leveled passages can be used for fluency development or timed-reading assessment.

Fluency Tip
Explicit directions tell students how to apply the fluency focus to the selection.

Word Counts
Numbers in the margin at the end of each line of the reading passage help in calculating words read per minute.

Name _____ **Date** _____

How's the Weather Up There?

I am **currently** 5 feet 11 inches tall, and I have been this height since I was 12 years old. When I was a young girl, I hated being tall. I always towered above the other students as we stood in line or walked to class. I was even taller than many of my teachers. However, now that I'm an adult, I don't mind it nearly so much.

At birth, I was 23 inches long. Since height is controlled by heredity, I know that I **inherited** this trait from my father. From as early as I can remember, people have been making comments about it. The teasing was often good-natured, but some of it was extremely hurtful.

In school, I was called the "Jolly Green Giant" and "Stork Legs," among other names. Going to buy clothes was one of the most **embarrassing** things I had to do because I could never find pants that were long enough. If they happened to reach my ankles, they were always too big around the waist.

My least favorite comment was "How's the weather up there?" My reaction was to slouch and sulk, hoping the person would leave me alone. Now when someone says that to me (and they often do), I respond differently. I reply with a confident smile, "Just fine, thanks!"

5
24
42
61
73
90
106
120
122
137
155
171
177
190
205
222
224

⚙ **FLUENCY TIP**

To practice reading with expression, read the second paragraph to a partner. Remember to read the last sentence with emotion.

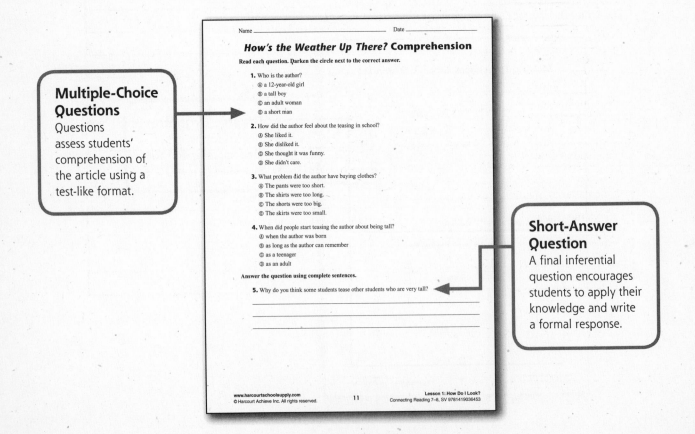

Multiple-Choice Questions
Questions assess students' comprehension of the article using a test-like format.

Short-Answer Question
A final inferential question encourages students to apply their knowledge and write a formal response.

Name _____ **Date** _____

How's the Weather Up There? Comprehension

Read each question. Darken the circle next to the correct answer.

1. Who is the author?
Ⓐ a 12-year-old girl
Ⓑ a tall boy
Ⓒ an adult woman
Ⓓ a short man

2. How did the author feel about the teasing in school?
Ⓐ She liked it.
Ⓑ She disliked it.
Ⓒ She thought it was funny.
Ⓓ She didn't care.

3. What problem did the author have buying clothes?
Ⓐ The pants were too short.
Ⓑ The shirts were too long.
Ⓒ The shorts were too big.
Ⓓ The skirts were too small.

4. When did people start teasing the author about being tall?
Ⓐ when the author was born
Ⓑ as long as the author can remember
Ⓒ as a teenager
Ⓓ as an adult

Answer the question using complete sentences.

5. Why do you think some students tease other students who are very tall?

_____
_____
_____

Correlation Chart

Reading Comprehension Skills

	Lesson
Asking questions	8
Building background	2
Cause and effect	11
Main idea and supporting details	6
Making connections	9
Making inferences	1, 13
Monitoring comprehension	4, 14
Problem and solution	10
Sequence	7, 15
Summarizing	5, 12
Visualizing	3

Fluency Skills

Expression	1, 6, 14, 15
Phrasing	2, 8, 9, 13
Punctuation	3, 4, 7, 10
Word accuracy	5, 11, 12

Science Standards

Describes the interactions between populations, natural disasters, and the environment	8, 11
Describes some cycles, structures, and processes that are found in a system	3, 7
Understands how body systems interact	5, 6, 7, 8
Identifies the role of scientific exploration and its impact	15
Recognizes the importance of technology in science	10

Social Studies Standards

Understands the contributions of people of various racial, ethnic, and religious groups	2, 12, 14
Understands the economic, political, cultural, and social processes that interact to shape patterns of human populations	2, 9, 12, 13, 14
Knows the characteristics and locations of important historical and contemporary societies	2, 13
Explores contemporary cultures and issues and their impact on society	1, 12, 14
Understands the importance of technology and its relationship with society	4

Connecting Reading 7–8, SV 9781419036453

Name _____ Date _____

Fluency Checklist

Circle the number to rate the reading.

Selection title _____			
	Very Good	**Good**	**Needs to Improve**
Word Reading Reads the words correctly	3	2	1
Rate of Reading Reads at a just-right rate— not too fast and not too slow	3	2	1
Expression Reads with expression	3	2	1
Phrasing Reads in groups of words— not word by word	3	2	1

Fluency Checklist
Connecting Reading 7–8, SV 9781419036453

Name _____   Date _____

Progress Record

Selection Title _____

Oral Reading Rating Circle the rating that best describes the student's phrasing, adherence to author's syntax, and expressiveness. (4 is highest)	4 3 2 1	
Last Word Read _____ **Number of Words Read**		
Error Tally		−
Words Correct per Minute (WCPM) Score	=	

Directions

1. Have a student read aloud the selection. Use a stopwatch or clock with a second hand to time the student. As the student reads, follow along on another photocopy of the story and unobtrusively make a mark in the Error Tally space for each error the student makes. Count mispronunciations, omissions, and substitutions as errors. Do not count repetitions or self-corrections as errors.

2. Have the student read the entire passage, but record the last word the student reads at the end of one minute. Alternatively, stop the student after one minute and record the last word read.

3. Rate the student's oral reading.

4. Use the last word read and the word count beside the last complete line read to determine the number of words read in one minute.

5. Subtract the error tally to calculate the WCPM score.

www.harcourtschoolsupply.com
© Harcourt Achieve Inc. All rights reserved.

7

Progress Record
Connecting Reading 7–8, SV 9781419036453

Lesson 1: How Do I Look?
Connecting Background

LEVELED TITLES

- *How's the Weather Up There?* — 5.6
- *Brace Face* — 7.0
- *Weird Wardrobe* — 8.0

Theme Notes

Heredity is the passing on of characteristics, or traits, from one generation to the next, or from parents to offspring. Heredity can determine how living things look and act. The three readings in this lesson cover topics related to inherited traits, including height and crooked teeth. One reading also looks at what is not inherited—clothing tastes.

Fluency Focus: Expression

Fluent readers use expression. They stress key words in a sentence to make the reading interesting and show what is important. Expression can also give different meanings to a sentence. Expressive reading means using a higher voice to end questions and saying important words longer, louder, or with a different voice.

Fluency Practice

Write this sentence on the board: *People say that I look just like my mother.*

Ask partners to read the sentence three times—to show sadness and happiness, and as a question.

Comprehension Focus: Making Inferences

Sometimes readers have to make inferences, or figure things out from clues in the selection. The author may not directly tell everything readers need to know. Sometimes authors give hints about the information, facts, and events in the text. Good readers think about the hints or clues that the author gives to help them understand the text and figure things out on their own. Students will be able to make inferences using the Making Inferences Graphic Organizer on page 9.

VOCABULARY

- *How's the Weather Up There?*
  currently
  inherited
  embarrassing

- *Brace Face*
  inherited
  trait
  orthodontist

- *Weird Wardrobe*
  eclectic
  unique
  stylish

www.harcourtschoolsupply.com
© Harcourt Achieve Inc. All rights reserved.

8

Lesson 1: How Do I Look?
Connecting Reading 7–8, SV 9781419036453

Making Inferences Graphic Organizer

Title _____

What the Text Says in Your Own Words

Quotation

Reasoning

What the Text Says in Your Own Words

Quotation

Reasoning

Lesson 1: How Do I Look?
Connecting Reading 7–8, SV 9781419036453

How's the Weather Up There?

	5

I am **currently** 5 feet 11 inches tall, and I have been this height since I was 12 years old. When I was a young girl, I hated being tall. I always towered above the other students as we stood in line or walked to class. I was even taller than many of my teachers. However, now that I'm an adult, I don't mind it nearly so much.

At birth, I was 23 inches long. Since height is controlled by heredity, I know that I **inherited** this trait from my father. From as early as I can remember, people have been making comments about it. The teasing was often good-natured, but some of it was extremely hurtful.

In school, I was called the "Jolly Green Giant" and "Stork Legs," among other names. Going to buy clothes was one of the most **embarrassing** things I had to do because I could never find pants that were long enough. If they happened to reach my ankles, they were always too big around the waist.

My least favorite comment was "How's the weather up there?" My reaction was to slouch and sulk, hoping the person would leave me alone. Now when someone says that to me (and they often do), I respond differently. I reply with a confident smile, "Just fine, thanks!"

24
42
61
73
90
106
120
122
137
155
171
177
190
205
222
224

⚙ FLUENCY TIP

To practice reading with expression, read the second paragraph to a partner. Remember to read the last sentence with emotion.

www.harcourtschoolsupply.com
© Harcourt Achieve Inc. All rights reserved.

10

Lesson 1: How Do I Look?
Connecting Reading 7–8, SV 9781419036453

Name _____ Date _____

How's the Weather Up There? Comprehension

Read each question. Darken the circle next to the correct answer.

1. Who is the author?

  Ⓐ a 12-year-old girl

  Ⓑ a tall boy

  Ⓒ an adult woman

  Ⓓ a short man

2. How did the author feel about the teasing in school?

  Ⓐ She liked it.

  Ⓑ She disliked it.

  Ⓒ She thought it was funny.

  Ⓓ She didn't care.

3. What problem did the author have buying clothes?

  Ⓐ The pants were too short.

  Ⓑ The shirts were too long.

  Ⓒ The shorts were too big.

  Ⓓ The skirts were too small.

4. When did people start teasing the author about being tall?

  Ⓐ when the author was born

  Ⓑ as long as the author can remember

  Ⓒ as a teenager

  Ⓓ as an adult

Answer the question using complete sentences.

5. Why do you think some students tease other students who are very tall?

_____

_____

_____

Lesson 1: How Do I Look?
Connecting Reading 7–8, SV 9781419036453

Brace Face

| | 2 |

Wearing braces is an experience that many people, especially kids, go through. After they wear braces for a couple of years, the metal comes off, though, and they have a perfectly beautiful smile.

So, like many of my fifth grade classmates, I got braces. We all had **inherited** the same **trait** from one of our parents—crooked teeth. Having braces means that food often gets stuck in your teeth, and your mouth is constantly in pain. You aren't allowed to munch on popcorn and other hard foods because you could bend or break a wire. And don't forget about the teasing, when people make comments like "tin grin" and "brace face."

After two years of having a metal grin, I got a plastic retainer that I was supposed to wear constantly, except while eating. However, I was embarrassed to talk at school because I sounded funny, and I couldn't sleep at night with it in my mouth. Obviously, I seldom wore my retainer.

When I was in seventh grade, I went for a dental checkup. The **orthodontist** could tell that I had neglected to wear my retainer, and she told me I would have to wear braces for an additional six months!

I learned my lesson, and I wore my retainer after that. Now that I'm older, I appreciate my smile, but I don't ever want to go through that awful experience again!

Line	Count
	15
	33
	35
	51
	66
	83
	100
	113
	131
	145
	163
	165
	181
	201
	204
	221
	235

⚙ FLUENCY TIP

When reading a personal account, pretend you are the person who is telling the story. Read this selection in a manner that shows you understand how that person was feeling.

Brace Face Comprehension

Read each question. Darken the circle next to the correct answer.

1. What do braces on the teeth do?

Ⓐ whiten them

Ⓑ straighten them

Ⓒ make them crooked

Ⓓ fill cavities

2. In which grade did the author get braces?

Ⓐ second grade

Ⓑ fifth grade

Ⓒ seventh grade

Ⓓ tenth grade

3. What is one problem with braces?

Ⓐ The metal breaks.

Ⓑ They make teeth brown.

Ⓒ They attract other metal things.

Ⓓ They slide around.

4. What might have been different if the author had worn the retainer as instructed?

Ⓐ The author would not have had to wear braces again.

Ⓑ The author would not have a beautiful smile.

Ⓒ The author would have kept crooked teeth.

Ⓓ The author would not have had to wear the retainer while sleeping.

Answer the question using complete sentences.

5. Do you think braces are worth the trouble? Explain.

_____

_____

_____

Connecting Reading 7–8, SV 9781419036453

Weird Wardrobe

From the time I could pick out my own clothes, I have had what many call an	2
"**eclectic**" taste in fashion. I enjoy mixing things up, setting trends, and steering clear of	19
	34

From the time I could pick out my own clothes, I have had what many call an "**eclectic**" taste in fashion. I enjoy mixing things up, setting trends, and steering clear of the styles that most of my peers wear.

In middle school and high school, I was "the girl with the weird wardrobe." I didn't care whether or not my wardrobe matched, and I certainly didn't care about other people's opinions. I often shopped at vintage boutiques and garage sales, looking for the perfect item to create interesting combinations.

My favorite outfits consisted of brightly colored trousers with bold patterns or prints. I would pair those with multicolored shoes, a wild, oversized shirt, and chunky jewelry. After raising an eyebrow, my relatives would ask how I developed my **unique** style, and I replied that it was in jeans, but definitely not in my genes. The truth is, sometimes my parents didn't want to be seen with me!

In college I studied fashion design, graduating at the top of my class. I designed clothing for the boutiques that I frequented, and my style remained the same—weird. Oddly enough, the people at the boutiques thought I looked **stylish**, as did the customers who were buying my clothes.

Today I design clothing for major television stars and recording artists. Although my work is done behind the scenes, sometimes I think, "If my classmates could see me now!"

Line counts
2
19
34
42
58
73
88
92
105
119
134
152
160
175
190
206
209
222
238

⚙ FLUENCY TIP

Sometimes when you see words in quotation marks, you should read those words by stressing your voice. For example, "I have had what many call an 'eclectic' taste in fashion."

Connecting Reading 7–8, SV 9781419036453

Weird Wardrobe Comprehension

Read each question. Darken the circle next to the correct answer.

1. Which clothing would be eclectic?

Ⓐ khaki shorts, sandals, blue shirt

Ⓑ black skirt, white blouse, black jewelry

Ⓒ red pants, yellow sweatshirt, pink hair scarf

Ⓓ blue jeans, red T-shirt, tennis shoes

2. Why didn't the author care about the opinion of others?

Ⓐ The author thought the clothes looked great.

Ⓑ The author didn't like the people at school.

Ⓒ The author was a rock star and was expected to dress in a weird way.

Ⓓ The author was the only one who knew about fashion.

3. How did the parents feel about the author's style?

Ⓐ They liked it.

Ⓑ They were angry about it.

Ⓒ They ignored it.

Ⓓ They were embarrassed.

4. How do you know the author is a successful designer?

Ⓐ She graduated from college.

Ⓑ People still tease her.

Ⓒ She still buys clothes at boutiques.

Ⓓ Famous people wear her clothes.

Answer the question using complete sentences.

5. How would you describe your style of clothing?

_____

_____

_____

Connecting Reading 7–8, SV 9781419036453

Lesson 2: Adventurers All
Connecting Background

LEVELED TITLES

- *Guard Duty* — 5.7
- *Thanksgiving Then and Now* — 7.1
- *Samoset, Squanto, and Massasoit* — 8.0

Theme Notes

In 1620, the Pilgrims crossed the Atlantic Ocean to North America. Some of them came for religious freedom, while others came for economic reasons. Some of them came simply for the love of adventure. The first year was difficult, though. This lesson details some of the events that year, including job responsibilities, the first Thanksgiving, and the help provided by some of the Native Americans.

Fluency Focus: Phrasing

Beginning readers look at each letter to know the sounds to say in a word. Fluent readers look at groups of words, or phrases, as they read sentences. Reading in chunks sounds more like natural speech. It also improves comprehension. Punctuation can help readers phrase correctly, but sometimes a reader must figure out phrasing independently.

Fluency Practice

Write this sentence on the board: *As you know, many Pilgrims perished the first year as a result of disease, starvation, and cold conditions.*

Model reading the sentence with and without correct phrasing. Discuss which sounds like natural speech. Invite partners to take turns reading the sentence.

Comprehension Focus: Building Background

Readers comprehend better when they know something about what they are reading. Knowing some background information helps them make connections between what they are reading and what they already know. Students will be able to build background using the graphic organizer on page 17.

VOCABULARY

- *Guard Duty*
  putrid
  compact
  perspective

- *Thanksgiving Then and Now*
  adequate
  challenged
  heritage

- *Samoset, Squanto, and Massasoit*
  inhabitants
  plague
  interpret

Name _____ Date _____

Building Background Graphic Organizer

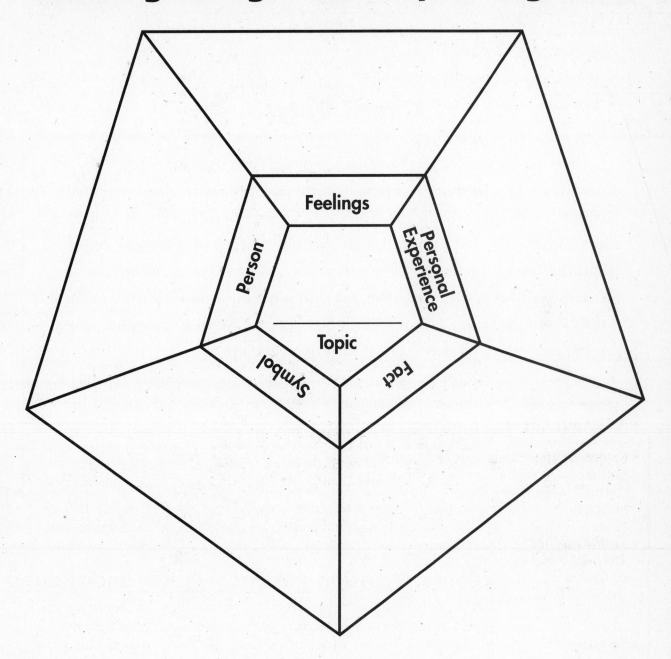

Feelings

Person

Personal Experience

_____
Topic

Symbol

Fact

Lesson 2: Adventurers All
Connecting Reading 7–8, SV 9781419036453

Guard Duty

| | 2 |

     I have had two forms of guard duty today, beginning with wolf duty last night. Since | 18

Squanto taught us to plant each corn kernel with a herring for fertilizer, the wolves have | 34

been prowling around our fields. They'd love to dig up those **putrid** fish and leave our corn | 51

plants to rot. So every Tuesday night, I stand guard over the garden and watch for wolves. | 68

If I see one, first I'm supposed to yell, and if that doesn't scare it, I'm supposed to shoot it. | 88

So far, I've only had to yell. I must admit, though, that it is spooky sitting alone in darkness, | 107

waiting for wolves. I have a difficult time staying awake, too, but I don't dare sleep. We are | 125

depending on the crops to keep us alive through the next winter. | 137

     At daybreak, I gathered eggs, drew water, weeded the kitchen garden, and helped pick | 151

greens for lunch. Now, as part of the **compact**, I'm posted to two hours' guard duty. From | 168

my **perspective**, I'm not sure what I'm guarding against, since the Native Americans have | 182

proved friendly, and the wolves sleep all day. | 190

⚙️ FLUENCY TIP

Pause at commas as you chunk each sentence into phrases. This is a good sentence for practice: "If I see one, first I'm supposed to yell, and if that doesn't scare it, I'm supposed to shoot it."

Guard Duty Comprehension

Read each question. Darken the circle next to the correct answer.

1. Why are the wolves near the fields?

Ⓐ They smell the fish.

Ⓑ They want to eat corn.

Ⓒ They want to scare the people away.

Ⓓ They are helping scare away birds.

2. What is the guard supposed to do first after seeing a wolf?

Ⓐ Run away.

Ⓑ Shoot it.

Ⓒ Yell loudly.

Ⓓ Trap it.

3. How does the author feel about daytime guard duty?

Ⓐ He thinks it's spooky.

Ⓑ He is happy to do it.

Ⓒ He hates it.

Ⓓ He thinks it's unnecessary.

4. Which is NOT a job of the author?

Ⓐ weeding the garden

Ⓑ guarding the crops

Ⓒ chopping wood

Ⓓ gathering eggs

Answer the questions using complete sentences.

5. What would you find the least attractive part of guard duty? Why?

_____

_____

_____

Thanksgiving Then and Now

4

Thanksgiving was celebrated a little differently by the Pilgrims than it is today. The | 18

first Thanksgiving in 1621 was a three-day event. The Pilgrims' first winter in the new land | 34

had been very difficult, but spring and summer were good. They had learned to plant crops, | 50

like corn and squash. As a result, they had **adequate** food to supply their needs for the | 67

coming winter. Moreover, the Pilgrims and Native Americans were learning to get along | 80

and trust each other. There was much to be thankful for, so the Pilgrims decided to have | 97

a huge celebration. | 100

During the feast, the Pilgrims served some of their vegetables. For meat, they had | 114

lobster, fish, and clams they got from the ocean, and wild turkeys and ducks they hunted. | 130

Ninety Native Americans joined them. They brought five deer. During the celebration, | 142

the Pilgrims and Native Americans **challenged** each other to games, like running and | 155

wrestling. The first Thanksgiving was a success. But the Pilgrims never had another | 168

Thanksgiving feast. | 170

The holiday as we know it today actually began during Civil War times. President | 184

Abraham Lincoln declared it a national holiday. Today, some families eat turkey, mashed | 197

potatoes, stuffing, and pumpkin pie. Other families include foods that are part of their | 211

cultural **heritage**. Many people watch football games on television. What do you think the | 225

Pilgrims would think of our yearly celebration? | 232

⚙ FLUENCY TIP

Read short sentences as one chunk. For example: "They brought five deer" is one chunk. Read longer sentences as several chunks. For example, read this sentence as shown: "The holiday / as we know it today / actually began / during Civil War times."

Thanksgiving Then and Now Comprehension

Read each question. Darken the circle next to the correct answer.

1. Which is NOT a reason the Pilgrims planned a feast?

Ⓐ They were friends with the Native Americans.

Ⓑ They had food for the winter.

Ⓒ They had decided to declare a national holiday.

Ⓓ Spring and summer had been good.

2. What did the Native Americans bring to the feast?

Ⓐ deer

Ⓑ ducks

Ⓒ squash

Ⓓ corn

3. How do you know the first Thanksgiving was a success?

Ⓐ It lasted three days.

Ⓑ The Pilgrims and Native Americans wrestled.

Ⓒ There was lots of food.

Ⓓ The Pilgrims never had another feast.

4. When did Thanksgiving as we know it begin?

Ⓐ when football started

Ⓑ during the Pilgrims' time

Ⓒ during the Civil War

Ⓓ when Lincoln was a boy

Answer the question using complete sentences.

5. What is the most important and meaningful part of Thanksgiving to you?

_____

_____

_____

Name _____ Date _____

Samoset, Squanto, and Massasoit

	4

In March of 1621, as the Pilgrims met to discuss how to protect themselves, a   19
Native American walked into the meeting. Imagine the Pilgrims' surprise when the man   32
addressed them in English. The man, Samoset, was from the Algonquin people. Samoset   45
explained that the Patuxet people, who had been **inhabitants** of the area, had been wiped   60
out by the **plague**.   64

A few days later, Samoset returned with Tisquantum, a Patuxet whom the Pilgrims   77
called Squanto. Squanto had traveled to England with an earlier English explorer and had   91
learned about the English culture. The Pilgrims asked Squanto to **interpret** for both sides in   106
a meeting between the Pilgrim leaders and Massasoit, the leader of the nearby Wampanoag   120
people. During the meeting, the leaders established a peace treaty that lasted for fifty years.   135

Squanto helped the Pilgrims adjust to the New World. He showed them how to plant   150
corn and fertilize it, as well as how to set snares to trap game. He also taught them how to   170
catch eels at low tide and cook them. Squanto died suddenly of a fever a few months after   188
interacting with the Pilgrims.   192

⚙ FLUENCY TIP

Practice phrasing by reading aloud the long sentences in this selection. Remember to read each phrase as one chunk.

Connecting Reading 7–8, SV 9781419036453

Samoset, Squanto, and Massasoit
Comprehension

Read each question. Darken the circle next to the correct answer.

1. How did the Pilgrims meet the Native Americans?

Ⓐ A Pilgrim was captured.

Ⓑ One Native American came to them.

Ⓒ The Pilgrims went to a tribe.

Ⓓ A Native American was taken hostage.

2. Where did Samoset most likely learn English?

Ⓐ in England

Ⓑ from the Pilgrims

Ⓒ from Squanto

Ⓓ from other English explorers

3. Which Native American had been to England?

Ⓐ Samoset

Ⓑ Squanto

Ⓒ Massasoit

Ⓓ Wampanoag

4. What did Squanto do to help the Pilgrims?

Ⓐ He made the other Native Americans respect the Pilgrims.

Ⓑ He taught them English.

Ⓒ He helped them with their food needs.

Ⓓ He showed them how to hunt with a bow.

Answer the question using complete sentences.

5. Which Native American had the biggest impact on the Pilgrims? Explain.

_____

_____

_____

Lesson 3: Stargazing
Connecting Background

LEVELED TITLES

- *Once in a Blue Moon — 4.1*
- *Why Do Stars Twinkle? — 5.3*
- *The Making of a Legend — 6.1*

Theme Notes

For centuries, the solar system was a puzzle. People would look up at the heavens and be amazed by the sun, stars, and moon. Little did they know what was actually out in the universe, past what their eyes could see. This lesson looks at the facts that explain some of the more interesting phenomena in the solar system, including blue moons, twinkling stars, and the making of astronomical legends.

Fluency Focus: Punctuation

Fluent readers use punctuation as a guide to how to read. They use ellipses, commas, semicolons, and dashes to alert themselves when to pause while reading longer sentences.

Fluency Practice

Write these words on the board: *An astronomer's job can be a fascinating one—one that is full of endless possibilities for discovering new planets, stars, and other heavenly bodies—whether he or she is brand new to the field or has been gazing through a telescope for many years.*

Read the sentence without pauses and then with pauses indicated by punctuation. Discuss which sounds better. Then have partners take turns reading the sentence fluently.

Comprehension Focus: Visualizing

Visualizing means that readers use the words they read or hear to paint pictures in their minds. These pictures help them imagine what a character, a place, or a thing looks like. Visualizing will help readers understand and remember what they read. The Visualizing Graphic Organizer on page 25 can help students better visualize the information in each text.

VOCABULARY

- *Once in a Blue Moon*
  expression
  atmosphere
  phenomenon

- *Why Do Stars Twinkle?*
  phenomenon
  refraction
  perceive

- *The Making of a Legend*
  justify
  satellite
  imaginative

Visualizing Graphic Organizer

| Word or phrase clue: | Word or phrase clue: | Word or phrase clue: | Word or phrase clue: |

The picture I visualize:

Once in a Blue Moon

"I haven't seen you in a blue moon." "We have steak once in a blue moon." The phrase *blue moon* is an **expression** commonly used in the English language. What does it mean, and is there really such a thing as a blue moon?

When enough dust or smoke collects in Earth's **atmosphere**, the moon can appear blue to an observer. For example, a volcano that exploded in Indonesia in 1883 shot a cloud of dust high into the atmosphere. The dust scattered the light reflected from the moon, giving it a blue hue. So, yes, there really is a scientific explanation for the moon appearing blue.

But sometimes we use the phrase for a moon that doesn't look blue. As you know, the moon revolves around Earth once about every 29 days. February usually has fewer than 29 days, and the other months have more than 29 days. Because of this pattern, we sometimes see two full moons in one month. When this **phenomenon** occurs, we call the second full moon a blue moon. The event actually happens about every 19 months—not too often. And that's exactly what *once in a blue moon* means—"not too often"!

5
23
38
49
62
78
93
110
112
129
144
160
176
192
204

⚙️ FLUENCY TIP

Remember that dashes are an interruption in a sentence. They are often used for emphasis and effect. Be sure to pause when you see them.

Name _____ Date _____

Once in a Blue Moon Comprehension

Read each question. Darken the circle next to the correct answer.

1. What event caused the moon to appear blue in 1883?

Ⓐ an earthquake

Ⓑ a volcano

Ⓒ a tsunami

Ⓓ a blizzard

2. What makes the moon look blue?

Ⓐ Dust scatters light reflected from the moon.

Ⓑ Earth casts a shadow on the moon.

Ⓒ Liquid in the atmosphere bends moonlight.

Ⓓ The moon can be seen in the daylight.

3. If a weather forecaster says there is a blue moon in the sky, what can you conclude?

Ⓐ There are two full moons in the same month.

Ⓑ There is a bad snowstorm coming.

Ⓒ A volcano is about to erupt.

Ⓓ February will have 29 days this year.

4. What does the following sentence mean?
"We have steak once in a blue moon."

Ⓐ We often eat steak.

Ⓑ We eat steak that is cooked until it is well done.

Ⓒ We seldom eat steak.

Ⓓ We eat steak only during a blue moon.

Answer the question using complete sentences.

5. When would you use the expression *once in a blue moon*?

_____

_____

_____

Connecting Reading 7–8, SV 9781419036453

Why Do Stars Twinkle?

4

How many times have you heard the popular children's song "Twinkle, Twinkle, Little   17

Star"? Probably almost as many times as there are stars. But did you ever stop to think   34

about just WHY stars appear to twinkle in the nighttime sky?   45

Imagine that Earth's atmosphere is like multiple layers of see-through blankets on a   58

bed. Then imagine that the stars are high above the blankets, and you are underneath all   74

those layers looking up. The blankets, or layers of air in the atmosphere, are constantly   89

moving. As the light from the stars passes through each blanket, or layer of the atmosphere,   105

the light bends. This bending is a scientific **phenomenon** called **refraction**. It is the same   120

action that makes a straw appear bent when you put it in a glass of water. Lots of layers in   140

the atmosphere cause continuous bending, which makes you **perceive** twinkling stars. Move   152

beyond the many layers of atmosphere where there is no air, and presto, the twinkling stops.   168

⚙ FLUENCY TIP

There are question marks in the first paragraph. Make sure you change your voice to reflect them. Read the text and then close your eyes, picturing the atmosphere and the twinkling stars. It will help you better understand and remember what you read.

Connecting Reading 7–8, SV 9781419036453

Name _____   Date _____

Why Do Stars Twinkle? Comprehension

Read each question. Darken the circle next to the correct answer.

1. How is Earth's atmosphere like blankets on a bed?

Ⓐ There are several layers.

Ⓑ They are made of wool.

Ⓒ Air is trapped between the layers.

Ⓓ They keep us from falling off Earth or out of bed.

2. Which is an example of *refraction*?

Ⓐ raindrops falling out of the sky

Ⓑ steam rising from a blacktop parking lot

Ⓒ a straw that looks broken in a glass of water

Ⓓ seeing your image in a mirror

3. What would the stars look like if you moved past the atmosphere?

Ⓐ lights that flicker every few minutes

Ⓑ dots of steady light

Ⓒ dark spots

Ⓓ quickly moving fireflies

4. What does *phenomenon* mean?

Ⓐ testing an idea

Ⓑ twinkling stars

Ⓒ learning a concept

Ⓓ an observable event

Answer the question using complete sentences.

5. What do you think you would see if you were above Earth's atmosphere? Draw a picture.

_____

_____

_____

The Making of a Legend

Imagine that you live in ancient China, and that in the middle of a normal day, the birds stop chirping and the daylight disappears. What would you think? What would you do? You would no doubt be terrified and might even think that the sun was gone forever. And once the daylight returned, not knowing the logical, scientific explanation for what occurred, you would make up a story to **justify** your experience. That is how legends, folklore, and myths are born.

In reality, what happened that day in ancient China was most likely a total solar eclipse. A solar eclipse happens when the moon, in its normal monthly orbit as Earth's **satellite**, comes between Earth and the sun, blocking out the sun's light. It lasts for about seven minutes. History is laden with folklore surrounding solar eclipses.

According to Chinese folklore, when an eclipse occurred, it meant a creature of some sort—perhaps a dragon—was trying to swallow the sun. Villagers beat drums and shot arrows into the atmosphere in order to chase the dragon away.

Although we now know what causes a solar eclipse, we still enjoy the **imaginative** and colorful explanation from ancient Chinese folklore.

5
22
37
54
67
83
86
102
117
133
142
156
171
182
197
203

⚙️ FLUENCY TIP

Be sure to use the punctuation in the first paragraph as a guide to phrasing sentences and making sense of the text.

The Making of a Legend Comprehension

Read each question. Darken the circle next to the correct answer.

1. What kind of eclipse did the legend try to explain?

Ⓐ lunar

Ⓑ solar

Ⓒ polar

Ⓓ sonar

2. Why did the birds stop chirping?

Ⓐ They thought it was nighttime.

Ⓑ They were scared.

Ⓒ They left and were migrating south.

Ⓓ They couldn't see to sing.

3. What caused the eclipse?

Ⓐ Earth blocked the light.

Ⓑ A man-made satellite blocked the light.

Ⓒ The stars blocked the light.

Ⓓ The moon blocked the light.

4. Why did villagers beat drums?

Ⓐ They hoped the noise would scare the creature away.

Ⓑ They hoped the noise would guide the sunlight back to Earth.

Ⓒ They hoped to chase the moon away.

Ⓓ They hoped the sound would reposition the sun and moon in the sky.

Answer the question using complete sentences.

5. Why might people need to create a story about something they cannot explain rationally or scientifically?

_____

_____

_____

Lesson 4: Radio Days
Connecting Background

LEVELED TITLES

- *Careers in Radio — 5.9*
- *Radio to the Rescue — 7.2*
- *From Wired to Wireless — 8.1*

Theme Notes

Radio revolutionized communications in the early 1900s. The first systems were actually signals sent from a wireless transmitter. It wasn't until after World War I that people realized that radios could provide information and entertainment throughout the country. In this lesson, the topics focus on careers in radio, a sea rescue, and the invention of the telegraph.

Fluency Focus: Punctuation

Fluent readers notice punctuation when they read. They know what punctuation means, and they use it to guide their reading. They pause at commas, ellipses, and dashes. They stop briefly at periods and change their voice for question marks and exclamation points.

Fluency Practice

VOCABULARY

- *Careers in Radio*
  personality
  compose
  opportunities

- *Radio to the Rescue*
  jolted
  trepidation
  grueling

- *From Wired to Wireless*
  devices
  persevered
  broadcasts

Write these unpunctuated sentences on the board: *By 1935 two-thirds of American homes had radios Adults listened to sports music comedies dramas mysteries and adventures Children listened to stories about Tarzan and the Lone Ranger.*

Have partners rewrite the sentences using correct punctuation and practice fluent reading.

Comprehension Focus: Monitoring Comprehension

Fluent readers monitor their comprehension while they read. They pause to think about the meaning of the selection and to ask questions to help themselves understand. If they do not understand a word, they use context clues and a dictionary to determine its meaning. The Word Meaning Map on page 33 can help students monitor comprehension through vocabulary development.

Word Meaning Map

Word	**Sentence**

I think the word means: _____

_____

The definition I found: _____

_____

A new sentence that shows the meaning: _____

_____

_____

Word	**Sentence**

I think the word means: _____

_____

The definition I found: _____

_____

A new sentence that shows the meaning: _____

_____

_____

Careers in Radio

3

19

38

54

61

76

94

113

118

133

149

164

167

180

198

214

222

237

244

Do you have a favorite DJ or sports announcer? What does the person do that makes you like him or her? People often choose a time to listen to the radio based on the radio host. While this person is important, there are often many support people at the station who make sure that the **personality** is successful!

The voice is one of the most important characteristics of a radio personality. Do you have a good voice? If so, then you might like to speak on the radio. You could broadcast the news or call the plays of sports events. You could also choose to play great music or tell jokes to make people laugh.

There are other jobs at the radio station that might interest you, too. Some people research and write the brief news stories you hear. Others create the jokes or **compose** the commercials that sell different products. Some people keep up with new music or get ideas for new shows.

Radio stations also need tech people, because they keep the machines running. They make sure the sound goes out loud and strong over the airways. This might just be the most important job at a radio station. Without the machines and the tech support, there would be no voices for us to enjoy—only silence!

Do any of these **opportunities** in radio sound interesting? If so, maybe one day you'll be part of a great radio show!

⚙ FLUENCY TIP

Exclamation points add excitement to sentences. When you read a sentence that ends in an exclamation point, use an energetic, excited tone.

Careers in Radio Comprehension

Read each question. Darken the circle next to the correct answer.

1. What is the main idea of this article?

Ⓒ Tech people fix problems at a station.

Ⓓ Stations need writers.

Ⓔ The DJ has the most important job at a station.

Ⓕ Many different people are needed to make a radio station successful.

2. What is the most important characteristic of a DJ?

Ⓒ telling jokes

Ⓓ having a good voice

Ⓔ playing good music

Ⓕ writing news reports

3. Why are commercials important to a radio station?

Ⓒ because they pay for the costs

Ⓓ because they entertain the listeners

Ⓔ because they are popular

Ⓕ because they use music

4. What might happen if a radio station did not have tech people?

Ⓒ The commercials would not be funny.

Ⓓ The station would play only sports events.

Ⓔ There might be no sound to listen to.

Ⓕ The devices would work all the time.

Answer the question using complete sentences.

5. Think about your favorite DJ or radio personality. What qualities does the person have that help him or her do the job?

_____

_____

_____

Radio to the Rescue

4

On January 22, 1909, the great ship *Republic* left New York with more than four   19

hundred passengers. A few hours later, a collision **jolted** passengers from their sleep.   32

Another ship, the *Florida*, had accidentally rammed the *Republic*. The crews of the ships   46

were unable to see each other in the dense, nighttime fog.   57

In 1909, not all ships had radio stations on board. Luckily, the *Republic* did, and the   73

operator was a man named Jack Binns. Binns had been sleeping a few feet from where the   90

Florida struck the ship.   94

What Binns saw filled him with **trepidation**. The steel wall of the radio room was   109

torn away. He remembered, "I could see nothing outside in the fog and the darkness."   124

Binns struggled to send out a message even as the room flooded: "REPUBLIC   137

RAMMED BY UNKNOWN STEAMSHIP—BADLY IN NEED OF ASSISTANCE."   146

He also radioed the ship's location.   152

Other ships heard Binns's message, and after thirteen hours of a **grueling** search   165

through the fog, the *Baltic* came to the rescue before the mighty ships sank. The *Baltic*   181

rescued not only the crew and passengers on the *Republic* but everyone on board the   196

Florida as well.   199

Later, people hailed Binns as a hero. The brave radio operator responded, "I only did   214

what I should have done."   219

⚙️ FLUENCY TIP

When you see quotation marks, think about who said the words and how the speaker would have said them. Match your tone and pace to how the speaker might have said the words.

Connecting Reading 7–8, SV 9781419036453

Radio to the Rescue Comprehension

Read each question. Darken the circle next to the correct answer.

1. Why did the *Florida* ram the *Republic*?

   Ⓐ They were fighting in a sea war.

   Ⓑ They could not see each other in the fog.

   Ⓒ The ocean currents pushed them together.

   Ⓓ The *Republic* radio operator didn't send out a location signal.

2. What happened after Binns radioed for help?

   Ⓐ Another ship came.

   Ⓑ People were jolted awake.

   Ⓒ It began to get really foggy.

   Ⓓ The *Florida* saved all the passengers on the *Republic*.

3. If you are filled with *trepidation*, how are you feeling?

   Ⓐ happy

   Ⓑ scared

   Ⓒ angry

   Ⓓ calm

4. What might have happened if Binns had not radioed for help?

   Ⓐ Many people would have drowned.

   Ⓑ The ships would have slowly sailed home.

   Ⓒ The crew would have repaired the ships.

   Ⓓ The passengers would have spent more time listening to music on the radio.

Answer the question using complete sentences.

5. Why do some people think Jack Binns is a hero?

   _____

   _____

   _____

From Wired to Wireless

4

Chances are that you have some handy devices that use wireless radio waves. | 17
Anytime you use a cell phone, watch a TV show, or open your garage door by pressing | 34
a button, you're using wireless radio waves. Thanks to the work of Italian scientist | 48
Guglielmo Marconi, radio waves make these **devices** work. | 56

Over a hundred years ago, Marconi began experimenting with radio waves by sending | 69
signals for short distances. He finally was able to send a signal about a mile and a half. | 87
Marconi then knew he could quickly send messages over even greater distances. Few people | 101
at the time agreed. They couldn't imagine sending messages through the air. Up to that | 116
time, people had been using telegraph wires. Yet Marconi **persevered**. He continued to | 129
increase the distance signals could be sent. | 136

1897: Marconi sends signals 11 miles. | 142

1898: Marconi sets up radio stations on ships. The ships communicate with each | 155
other from a distance of 75 miles. | 162

1901: Marconi **broadcasts** signals across the Atlantic Ocean. | 170

Today, wireless radio waves still link the world—and beyond. | 180

🛠 FLUENCY TIP

As you read each year in the time line, pause at the colon. Then read the information that follows in a voice that tells listeners that the information is important.

From Wired to Wireless Comprehension

Read each question. Darken the circle next to the correct answer.

1. Which device does NOT use a radio wave?

Ⓐ TV remote

Ⓑ cell phone

Ⓒ wireless Internet

Ⓓ dishwasher

2. What did Guglielmo Marconi experiment with?

Ⓐ sending signals through the air

Ⓑ inventing the telegraph

Ⓒ receiving messages through telegraph wires

Ⓓ making cell phones work in all areas

3. What does a person do if he or she *perseveres*?

Ⓐ experiments

Ⓑ gives up

Ⓒ keeps trying

Ⓓ gets excited

4. What important event happened after ships radioed to each other?

Ⓐ Marconi sent signals 11 miles.

Ⓑ Marconi set up radios on several ships.

Ⓒ Marconi invented telephones.

Ⓓ Marconi sent signals across the Atlantic Ocean.

Answer the question using complete sentences.

5. Why was it hard to convince people in Marconi's day that wireless communication would work?

_____

_____

_____

Lesson 4: Radio Days
Connecting Reading 7–8, SV 9781419036453

Lesson 5: You Are What You Eat

Connecting Background

LEVELED TITLES

- *Diets: The Good and the Bad — 6.0*
- *Get Off the Couch! — 7.3*
- *Your New Food Guide — 8.2*

Theme Notes

Research suggests that food does more than give you energy. Evidence is mounting that the food you eat can have a profound effect on how you feel and behave. For example, excessive carbohydrates can make you tired, and proteins enhance alertness. This lesson further examines some important facts relating to nutrition, diet, and exercise.

Fluency Focus: Word Accuracy

Fluent readers read with accuracy. They learn how to pronounce difficult words, and they learn what they mean. They do not skip or add words either. When reading words accurately, fluent readers sound out unfamiliar words and decide whether the words make sense. They use a dictionary to help them understand the words.

Fluency Practice

Write the sentences below on the board:

- *Let's go dime in that restaurant.*
- *The food will leave stain on your shirt.*
- *Please hand me that the plate.*

Ask partners to rewrite the sentences without mistakes and practice reading them.

Comprehension Focus: Summarizing

When people summarize, they make a long story short. They restate important ideas in their own words. To best summarize, readers often take notes, listing the most important idea from each paragraph, section, or page. The Summarizing Notes graphic organizer on page 41 can help students identify the important information in each paragraph of the text.

VOCABULARY

- *Diets: The Good and the Bad*
  appetizing
  consumes
  lean

- *Get Off the Couch!*
  aerobic
  conversely
  anaerobic

- *Your New Food Guide*
  obesity
  nutritional
  refined

Name _____ Date _____

Summarizing Notes

Paragraph 1 _____
_____
_____

Paragraph 2 _____
_____
_____

Paragraph 3 _____
_____
_____

Paragraph 4 _____
_____
_____

Article Summary _____
_____
_____

Lesson 5: You Are What You Eat
Connecting Reading 7–8, SV 9781419036453

Name _____   Date _____

Diets: The Good and the Bad

6

Have you ever heard of the cabbage soup diet or the all-liquid diet? They don't sound   22
very **appetizing**, do they? You probably have heard about the no-carb diet, too. All these   37
eating practices are ways for a person to lose weight—but beware! Following a diet that   53
cuts out an entire type of food is not healthy, and skimping on calories is not the way to go,   73
either. Eating just one food can be quite dangerous.   82

Yet these are the extreme behaviors that fad diets require. Fad diets are like any other   98
fashion or craze. They're in for a while, and then they're out. However, they don't hold up   115
over time because they don't work! Sure, people may lose weight for a week or two, but over   133
time, the excess pounds return.   138

Generally, everyone attempts to diet at one time or another. A diet is simply controlling   153
the foods a person **consumes**. The best and most successful way to lose weight in the long   170
run is to eat a healthy and balanced diet, which means eating foods from all the major food   188
groups. You should choose a variety of fruits, vegetables, and grains, especially whole   201
grains. Also, include a daily mix of **lean** proteins, like chicken or fish, and low-fat dairy   217
products, such as yogurt and skim milk. And don't forget to exercise several times each   232
week to keep your muscles and bones strong. Now that's a lifelong diet you can live with!   249

⚙️ FLUENCY TIP

The final paragraph has some hard words, such as *consumes* and *lean*. Read them
carefully so you don't say the wrong word.

Name _____   Date _____

Diets: The Good and the Bad Comprehension

Read each question. Darken the circle next to the correct answer.

1. Why might eating only one kind of food be unhealthy?

Ⓐ The taste buds stop working.

Ⓑ The body is not getting nutrients from all food groups.

Ⓒ The body is getting too many nutrients.

Ⓓ The body learns to process only that kind of food.

2. What is a fad diet?

Ⓐ a way to eat that is popular

Ⓑ a healthy choice of foods

Ⓒ eating only one kind of food

Ⓓ not eating enough food

3. Which is the best way to lose weight?

Ⓐ Eat foods high in fat.

Ⓑ Eat only fruits.

Ⓒ Eat from all food groups and exercise.

Ⓓ Exercise and don't worry about food.

4. Which is an example of protein?

Ⓐ liquid

Ⓑ chicken

Ⓒ cabbage

Ⓓ apple

Answer the question using complete sentences.

5. Are all fad diets a bad thing? Explain.

_____

_____

_____

Get Off the Couch!

| | 4 |

Do you shoot hoops, dance for hours, climb stairs, walk your dog, or rush to catch up with a friend? You probably don't realize it, but you are frequently exercising. Because of the movement, your muscles get stronger and can do everything you need them to do.

When you swim a few laps, jump rope, or sprint to the corner, your heart and breathing quicken. Most likely, you get sweaty, too! You're doing **aerobic** exercise, which strengthens your heart muscle. *Aerobic* means "with air," and aerobic exercise requires oxygen. When your heart gets this kind of workout, it becomes more effective at delivering oxygen to your body.

Conversely, when you do push-ups, carry a heavy box, or lift weights, your body needs strength rather than oxygen. Now you're doing **anaerobic** exercise. *Anaerobic* means "without air," so an anaerobic exercise does not require oxygen, but it builds strong bones and muscles.

Whether aerobic or anaerobic, exercise is a good thing that helps your body function properly and stay healthy. So get off the couch and move!

Line counts
21
36
51
67
80
92
107
111
125
137
152
154
168
179

⚙ FLUENCY TIP

If you can't pronounce *aerobic* or *anaerobic*, look them up in a dictionary to learn their pronunciations before you read.

Name _____   Date _____

Get Off the Couch! Comprehension

Read each question. Darken the circle next to the correct answer.

1. What happens when you exercise?

    Ⓐ Your muscles get stronger.

    Ⓑ Your muscles get longer.

    Ⓒ Your muscles always get air.

    Ⓓ Your muscles never get air.

2. Which is an example of an aerobic exercise?

    Ⓐ lifting weights

    Ⓑ playing tug-of-war

    Ⓒ watching television

    Ⓓ walking the dog

3. Which kind of exercise builds bones?

    Ⓐ aerobic

    Ⓑ anaerobic

    Ⓒ zoophobic

    Ⓓ doraphobic

4. Why should you want to strengthen the heart muscle?

    Ⓐ It helps you love more people.

    Ⓑ It helps you lift more weight.

    Ⓒ Your heart will get softer.

    Ⓓ Your heart will pump more oxygen.

Answer the question using complete sentences.

5. Do you get enough exercise? Explain. If not, tell what you could do to change your habits.

    _____

    _____

    _____

Lesson 5: You Are What You Eat
Connecting Reading 7–8, SV 9781419036453

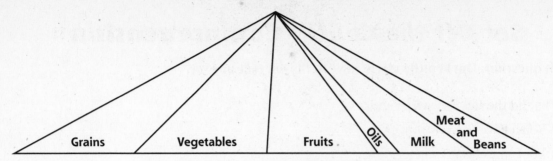

Your New Food Guide

4

The U.S. Department of Agriculture (USDA) revised the food guide pyramid in order to clarify the daily choices you must make to achieve good health. A main goal of the revision is to curb the ever-increasing **obesity** rate among young people. *Obesity* means "very overweight." Unfortunately, many young people are making poor food choices and getting too little exercise, which often leads to obesity and poor health.

16

32

46

57

71

The USDA advises daily choices from all five food groups. However, you should eat less from some food groups and more from others. Notice that the bands for meats and oils are narrower than the others. The size reflects the USDA suggestion that you consume less of these foods and more of the others, such as whole grains, fruits, vegetables, and low-fat dairy products.

84

100

115

130

135

The USDA cautions that not all foods within a food group are of equal **nutritional** value. For example, the guidelines suggest you eat more whole-wheat bread and less **refined** white bread. While they are both grains, they have different nutritional values.

150

163

176

If you follow these guidelines and exercise, you should be on your way to better health.

191

192

⚙ FLUENCY TIP

Before you read, look for any difficult words and be sure you can say them.

Your New Food Guide Comprehension

Read each question. Darken the circle next to the correct answer.

1. Why did the USDA change the food guide pyramid?

Ⓐ to tell people to eat less fruit

Ⓑ to explain how to diet

Ⓒ to better explain the foods people should eat

Ⓓ to guide people to eat less food

2. From which food group should you eat the most?

Ⓐ oils

Ⓑ sweets

Ⓒ meats

Ⓓ grains

3. Which is a healthy snack?

Ⓐ chips and milk

Ⓑ apple and peanut butter

Ⓒ carrots and soda

Ⓓ candy and pizza

4. What is a *refined* food?

Ⓐ processed

Ⓑ good tasting

Ⓒ oily

Ⓓ healthy

Answer the questions using complete sentences.

5. What did you eat for dinner last night? Was it a healthy meal? Explain.

_____

_____

_____

Lesson 6: Eye Witness
Connecting Background

LEVELED TITLES

- *Caring for the Eyes* — 6.1
- *Braille* — 7.5
- *Diseases of the Eye* — 8.2

Theme Notes

From the time people wake in the morning until they go to sleep at night, their eyes are at work. Eyes receive information about the world around them and send that information to the brain. This lesson focuses on eye care, the Braille language, and diseases of the eye.

Fluency Focus: Expression

Fluent readers focus on expression, or feelings, as they read. Reading with expression makes the selection more interesting and helps improve understanding. Sometimes, the reader needs to think about the meaning of a sentence before reading to decide which parts are important. Then the reader should use tone and rhythm to stress those words to emphasize meaning.

Fluency Practice

Write these sentences on the board: *Did you hear that a ball hit Sheila in the eye? She went to the doctor. Thank goodness her eye will be OK!*

Discuss the purpose of the punctuation. Have volunteers read the sentences expressively.

Comprehension Focus: Main Idea and Supporting Details

While they are reading, it is important for readers to determine and understand the main idea of the selection. A topic is what the selection is about. The main idea is the writer's most important point about the topic. The writer may not state the main idea directly. Readers may have to figure it out by studying the details. Students can use the Main Idea and Supporting Details Graphic Organizer on page 49 to help them as they read the selections.

VOCABULARY

- *Caring for the Eyes*
  optometrist
  ophthalmologist
  prescribes

- *Braille*
  technique
  recognized
  interfere

- *Diseases of the Eye*
  surgically
  nourishment
  inflammation

Name _____ Date _____

Main Idea and Supporting Details Graphic Organizer

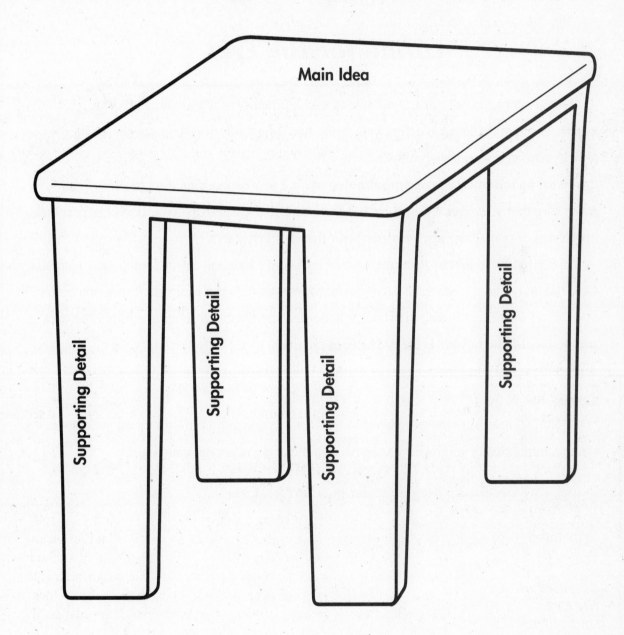

Main Idea

Supporting Detail

Supporting Detail

Supporting Detail

Supporting Detail

Connecting Reading 7–8, SV 9781419036453

Name _____   Date _____

Caring for the Eyes

| | 4 |

Most people do not think about taking care of their eyes. However, sight is an | 19
important function, and protecting your eyes should be a priority. Here are some tips | 33
to help you keep your eyes healthy. | 40

Visit an **optometrist** or **ophthalmologist** for a yearly checkup. An eye doctor can | 53
make sure that your eyes are healthy and that you can see clearly. If your doctor **prescribes** | 70
eyeglasses or contact lenses, wear them as often as suggested. | 80

Eat a balanced diet by drinking a lot of milk and water and eating fruits and vegetables. | 97
Give the body enough rest each night. Eyes that are healthy and well rested function better. | 113

Never look directly into the sun. Light comes into the eye through the pupil, the dark | 129
spot in the middle of your eyeball. The eyes are made to see only certain types of light, and | 148
sunlight is too bright for your eyes to handle. You should also wear sunglasses on bright | 164
days to further protect your eyes from the bright light. | 174

Finally, make sure there is plenty of light when you read. Dim light often makes you | 190
strain the muscles in your eyes. Excessive strain can also damage your sight. | 203

 FLUENCY TIP

To practice reading with expression, read the first paragraph to a partner. What tone of voice do you think fits the purpose of the paragraph?

Caring for the Eyes Comprehension

Read each question. Darken the circle next to the correct answer.

1. What is the main idea of this article?

Ⓐ It is important to keep your eyes healthy.

Ⓑ A balanced diet can keep your eyes healthy.

Ⓒ Looking at the sun can damage your eyes.

Ⓓ Use a lamp when reading at night.

2. What is an *ophthalmologist*?

Ⓐ a part of the eye

Ⓑ an eye disease

Ⓒ an eye doctor

Ⓓ eyeglasses

3. How does sleep affect the eyes?

Ⓐ It does not help or hurt them.

Ⓑ It rests them.

Ⓒ It protects the eyes from too much light.

Ⓓ Too much sleep results in reduced vision.

4. Which is NOT a healthy eye practice?

Ⓐ eating a balanced diet

Ⓑ using a lamp while reading in dim light

Ⓒ looking directly at the light

Ⓓ wearing sunglasses in bright sunlight

Answer the question using complete sentences.

5. How do people who have limited or no sight compensate for their loss?

_____

_____

_____

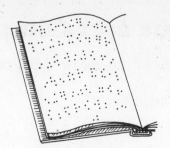

Braille

Braille is a system of writing and printing for people who are blind. Louis Braille	1
	16

Braille is a system of writing and printing for people who are blind. Louis Braille |16
developed the system when he was only 15 years old. At age 3, Louis Braille injured his |33
eye in an accident with his father's tools. After an infection, he lost the vision in both of his |52
eyes. He attended a school for blind people, where he learned to read raised letters. While |68
the system worked, Braille wanted a faster way to read, so he adapted a **technique** a French |85
Army officer had used for nighttime battlefield communication. |93

Braille's system consists of 6 raised dots, which are arranged in 63 different |106
combinations. From just 6 dots, Braille was able to develop an alphabet, punctuation marks, |120
numbers, and a system for writing music. People can read Braille by running their fingertips |135
lightly across the raised dots. The raised dots are created using a hand tool or a 6-key |152
machine called a *braillewriter*. This system is **recognized** as the official written language |165
of blind people around the world. |171

In the 1960s, publishers began using computers to increase production of Braille books. |184
Braille books have dots on both sides of the paper. Dots on one side of the page do not |203
interfere with dots on the other side. |210

⚙️ **FLUENCY TIP**

When reading factual information, your voice will show a little less expression. Stress key words in a factual sentence, for example: "After an INFECTION, he lost the VISION in BOTH of his eyes."

Braille Comprehension

Read each question. Darken the circle next to the correct answer.

1. What is this article mostly about?

Ⓐ the life of Louis Braille

Ⓑ the development of the Braille system

Ⓒ how to produce Braille textbooks

Ⓓ how people who are blind read

2. At what age did Braille develop his writing system?

Ⓐ 3

Ⓑ 15

Ⓒ 30

Ⓓ 63

3. What is the basis of the Braille system?

Ⓐ the shapes of three triangles

Ⓑ the order of alphabet letters

Ⓒ battlefield codes

Ⓓ the different arrangements of 6 dots

4. Why is there an official language for people who are blind?

Ⓐ People who are blind want to send messages that sighted people cannot read.

Ⓑ People will buy more braillewriters.

Ⓒ People around the world can communicate with each other.

Ⓓ People will have more books to read.

Answer the question using complete sentences.

5. How has Louis Braille's system changed life for people who are blind?

_____

_____

_____

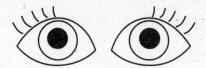

Diseases of the Eye

Disease can affect any part of the eye, and most instances of blindness are caused by eye disease, while the rest are caused by injuries. Though there are many diseases of the eye, cataract, glaucoma, and conjunctivitis are among the most common.

Cataract is a condition in which the lens of the eye becomes cloudy. If the cloudiness covers a large area or is at the center of the lens, blindness can occur. Some cataracts cause little or no loss of vision, and most are a result of aging. The lens can often be **surgically** removed and replaced.

Glaucoma occurs when the fluid that provides **nourishment** to the cornea and the lens does not drain properly. This increases pressure in the eye and, if left untreated, destroys the optic nerve. Treatments include eyedrops, pills, or laser therapy, which must be maintained throughout life.

Conjunctivitis is an **inflammation** of the membrane that lines the eyelids and covers part of the eyeball. Some types of the disease are called pinkeye and may be caused by an infection or an allergy. Doctors usually treat conjunctivitis with eyedrops.

4
20
36
46
62
80
99
102
116
132
145
147
160
178
188

⚙ FLUENCY TIP

Preview the pronunciation of words in bold type so you can pronounce them correctly and read them fluently. This will help you read with better expression.

Diseases of the Eye Comprehension

Read each question. Darken the circle next to the correct answer.

1. How can a cataract be corrected?

Ⓐ Eyedrops remove the disease.

Ⓑ The lens is replaced.

Ⓒ Glasses correct the vision.

Ⓓ Lasers reshape the eyeball.

2. What is glaucoma?

Ⓐ Fluid in the eye increases pressure.

Ⓑ The lens is cloudy.

Ⓒ The eye is pink.

Ⓓ The membrane in the eye swells.

3. What happens to a part of the body when it develops an inflammation?

Ⓐ It produces too much fluid.

Ⓑ It swells up.

Ⓒ It gets cloudy.

Ⓓ It becomes hard.

4. What is one cause of conjunctivitis?

Ⓐ infection

Ⓑ surgery

Ⓒ a blow to the eye

Ⓓ aging

Answer the questions using complete sentences.

5. Which eye disease seems the most severe? Why?

_____

_____

_____

Lesson 7: A Look Inside
Connecting Background

- *The Circulatory System — 6.2*
- *The Digestive System — 7.5*
- *The Nervous System — 8.5*

Theme Notes

The human body is an amazing machine. It is made up of organs, muscles, tissues, and fluids that form different systems. In this lesson, readers explore the circulatory system, nervous system, and digestive system to learn about the workings of the body.

Fluency Focus: Punctuation

Fluent readers know what punctuation is and what it stands for. They know to change the way they read based on the punctuation. They look for punctuation instead of skipping the marks and racing forward. Fluent readers stop at periods and pause at commas. They use a questioning voice for question marks and excitement at exclamation points.

Fluency Practice

VOCABULARY

- *The Circulatory System*
  absorbs
  arteries
  amazingly

- *The Digestive System*
  concoction
  flexible
  masticated

- *The Nervous System*
  automatic
  analyze
  milliseconds

Write these sentences on the board: *"Don't eat that, Abby!" Kyle shouted. "Don't you see the mold on the other side? It could make you really sick."*

Point out the punctuation. Then have partners take turns reading the sentences with proper expression.

Comprehension Focus: Sequence

Sequence is the order in which events happen. Science articles often use sequence to tell the steps in a process. A flowchart can show the order of the steps. Time-order words, such as *first*, *next*, *afterwards*, and *meanwhile*, give clues about the steps. The Flowchart on page 57 can help students understand the process in each selection.

www.harcourtschoolsupply.com
56
Lesson 7: A Look Inside
Connecting Reading 7–8, SV 9781419036453

Name _____ Date _____

Flowchart

Process _____

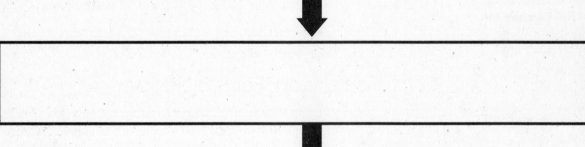

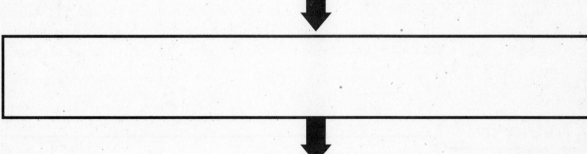

Lesson 7: A Look Inside
Connecting Reading 7–8, SV 9781419036453

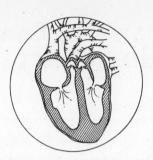

The Circulatory System

	3

The word *circulatory* comes from the word *circle*. In the human circulatory system, | 16

blood is pumped from the heart to the other parts of the body and then returns to the heart. | 35

For such a powerful organ, the adult heart is really quite small. Actually, it measures only | 51

about the size of a fist. | 57

When the blood circulates, it travels first to the lungs, where it **absorbs** oxygen. Red | 72

blood cells carry the oxygen back to the heart and then out again to other parts of the | 90

human body. The blood going out from the heart travels through tubes called **arteries**. In its | 106

trip back to the heart, blood flows through tubes called veins. The whole trip actually takes | 122

less than two minutes to complete the circle. **Amazingly**, by the time you are seventy years | 138

old, your heart will have beaten over two and a half billion times! | 151

⚙ FLUENCY TIP

The words *circulatory* and *circle* are written in italics. The italics show that the author wants to explain something about the word itself. So read the words without stress or pause.

The Circulatory System Comprehension

Read each question. Darken the circle next to the correct answer.

1. What is the main organ in the circulatory system?

Ⓐ fist

Ⓑ arteries

Ⓒ lungs

Ⓓ heart

2. Why did the author write this article?

Ⓐ to make people laugh

Ⓑ to tell a funny story

Ⓒ to persuade

Ⓓ to explain something

3. Why is the name *circulatory system* a good one?

Ⓐ The heart has a circular shape.

Ⓑ The blood circles through the body.

Ⓒ The veins form a circle.

Ⓓ The organs circulate through the body.

4. Where does the blood get oxygen?

Ⓐ lungs

Ⓑ veins

Ⓒ stomach

Ⓓ brain

Answer the question using complete sentences.

5. What might happen if oxygen didn't circulate in the body?

_____

_____

_____

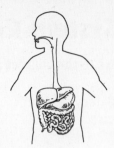

The Digestive System

3

19

32

48

66

81

88

101

117

131

146

150

164

180

196

204

You take your first bite of an apple and close your eyes, savoring its crispness and sweetness. Did you know that digestion begins as your teeth crush the apple?

Our bodies must convert all the food we eat into nutrients we can absorb and energy we can use. We use our teeth to crush the food into smaller pieces. These pieces then mix with our saliva, which breaks the food down further. This food **concoction** travels through a series of **flexible** tubes—our digestive system.

First, the **masticated** food travels down the esophagus into the stomach, where food is churned and mixed with stomach acids to process it even more. From the stomach, the food mixture travels through the small intestine. Ironically, the small intestine is the largest internal organ of the body. An average small intestine, when stretched out, is between 20 and 25 feet long!

After leaving the small intestine, the food travels through the large intestine. By this time, the nutrients from your apple have been absorbed by your blood system at every step in the process. What remains of the digested apple is considered waste. In all, the entire digestive process takes approximately 30 to 40 hours.

⚙ FLUENCY TIP

The last sentence in the third paragraph has two commas that "set off" a phrase. Be sure to pause.

Lesson 7: A Look Inside
Connecting Reading 7–8, SV 9781419036453

The Digestive System Comprehension

Read each question. Darken the circle next to the correct answer.

1. When does digestion start?

Ⓐ when the teeth crush the food

Ⓑ when the saliva flows into the mouth

Ⓒ after the food leaves the mouth

Ⓓ after the food enters the stomach

2. What does digestion do?

Ⓐ passes oxygen through the body

Ⓑ senses the food

Ⓒ breaks the food into nutrients

Ⓓ makes the body grow

3. What is *masticated* food?

Ⓐ nutrient rich

Ⓑ chewed

Ⓒ fatty

Ⓓ inedible

4. Where does the food travel after leaving the esophagus?

Ⓐ small intestine

Ⓑ large intestine

Ⓒ stomach

Ⓓ saliva

Answer the question using complete sentences.

5. How are nutrients from food passed to the body?

_____

_____

_____

Connecting Reading 7–8, SV 9781419036453

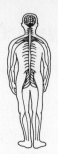

The Nervous System

3

19

32

48

65

78

91

100

118

133

149

166

180

When a U.S. spaceship travels into space, it is controlled by the command center at the National Aeronautics and Space Administration, or NASA. Think of your nervous system as the command center of your body. Your brain, spinal cord, and thousands of nerves are part of this command center. Some of the nerves in the control center are in charge of **automatic** functions, such as your heartbeat, your breathing, and your digestion. The other nerves gather data about what's happening around you, **analyze** the information, and send out information that helps you respond appropriately to the situation.

Let's say that you're about to touch a hot stove. As your hand gets close to the heat, the nerves in your fingertips send this information to your brain through your spinal cord. Your brain recognizes the danger of touching a hot stove and wants to protect you. Within **milliseconds**, it sends a message back down your spinal cord and out to your finger at 250 miles an hour. You jerk your finger just in time and don't get burned.

 FLUENCY TIP

NASA is an acronym, a word formed from the initial letters of a longer term. Read an acronym just like any other word.

The Nervous System Comprehension

Read each question. Darken the circle next to the correct answer.

1. What organ serves as part of the body's command center?

Ⓐ heart

Ⓑ lungs

Ⓒ brain

Ⓓ fingers

2. Which is an automatic function in the body?

Ⓐ walking

Ⓑ blinking

Ⓒ seeing

Ⓓ talking

3. In what order do the signals move?

Ⓐ brain, fingertips, spinal cord

Ⓑ spinal cord, fingertips, brain

Ⓒ fingertips, brain, spinal cord

Ⓓ brain, spinal cord, fingertips

4. According to the article, what does the brain recognize?

Ⓐ metal

Ⓑ heat

Ⓒ skin

Ⓓ sharp

Answer the question using complete sentences.

5. What might happen if a group of nerve cells in a part of your body stopped working correctly?

_____

_____

_____

Lesson 7: A Look Inside

Connecting Reading 7–8, SV 9781419036453

Lesson 8: Science to the Rescue
Connecting Background

Theme Notes

At one time or another, everyone gets a cold. A cold is caused by a virus. Viruses are all over the place and enter the body through the nose, mouth, or cuts in the skin. They attack healthy cells, causing a variety of illnesses and diseases, some of which can be deadly. This lesson explores some viruses, including malaria, smallpox, and measles.

Fluency Focus: Phrasing

When reading word-for-word, readers may not understand the meaning of a sentence. Focusing on punctuation can help a reader phrase, or chunk, words so that the text makes sense, thereby improving comprehension. At times, readers will have to figure out the phrasing on their own. The key is to determine which words look and sound like they go together.

Fluency Practice

Write these sentences on the board: *People need to cover their mouth when they cough and their nose when they sneeze. These simple actions will often prevent the spread of germs, thus helping others stay healthy.*

Challenge partners to rewrite the sentences and put a slash between each natural-sounding phrase. Have them read the sentences fluently.

Comprehension Focus: Asking Questions

Good readers pause to ask questions about what they read. Asking questions is a great way to check understanding. What kinds of questions should readers ask? Start with the *5-W and How* questions: *Who? What? When? Where? Why?* and *How?* Listing questions on the Asking Questions Chart on page 65 can help students track concepts that are unclear. Then readers know they need to reread those sentences or sections.

VOCABULARY

- *Mosquito Bites*
  microbes
  treatment
  vaccine

- *Smallpox*
  antibodies
  immune
  microbes

- *Measles*
  vaccine
  compromised
  contagious

Name _____   Date _____

Asking Questions Chart

	Questions					
Page						
Who?	What?	When?	Where?	Why?	How?	

Lesson 8: Science to the Rescue
Connecting Reading 7–8, SV 9781419036453

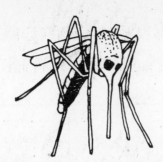

Mosquito Bites

| | 2 |

The female mosquito is hungry for blood. She isn't picky, so she chooses any animal she can find. After landing on the skin of her victim, her mouth, which has needle-like parts, pierces her victim's skin. As she sucks up blood through her mouth, her saliva drips into the victim's skin. The saliva carries **microbes**, or germs, which enter the victim's bloodstream.

Sometimes a mosquito bite causes nothing more than a puffy, red itch. However, the germs from a bite can make people very sick or, at times, even kill.

Some bites spread a deadly sickness called malaria. Malaria has hurt millions of people worldwide. Medicines can cure it if doctors treat it right away. Without **treatment**, many people die. Researchers are working on a **vaccine** that may someday prevent the disease.

Mosquitoes also carry a harmful germ called the West Nile virus. Researchers are studying ways to prevent and treat the sickness it causes as well.

Line count
17
33
49
63
64
78
92
106
120
134
147
159

⚙ FLUENCY TIP

Look at the second paragraph. Put a slash (/) between each phrase. Now practice your phrasing by rereading the paragraph.

Mosquito Bites Comprehension

Read each question. Darken the circle next to the correct answer.

1. Which kind of mosquito bites?

Ⓐ larva

Ⓑ nymph

Ⓒ adult female

Ⓓ adult male

2. Which part of the mosquito carries the germs?

Ⓐ skin

Ⓑ saliva

Ⓒ feet

Ⓓ blood

3. What is the most common reaction to a mosquito bite?

Ⓐ itchy bump

Ⓑ stinging bump

Ⓒ flat, red spot

Ⓓ puffy, brown spot

4. Which harmful disease might a mosquito carry?

Ⓐ smallpox

Ⓑ flu

Ⓒ measles

Ⓓ malaria

Answer the question using complete sentences.

5. What can you do to reduce your chance of getting a mosquito bite?

_____

_____

_____

Lesson 8: Science to the Rescue
Connecting Reading 7–8, SV 9781419036453

Smallpox

	1

Named for its small pus-filled bumps, smallpox once killed half the people it
infected. Today the disease kills no one. In fact, the smallpox virus infects no one.
Through the discovery and use of vaccines, people have eliminated smallpox.

The British physician Dr. Edward Jenner found a way to prevent smallpox. He
noticed that farmhands who caught cowpox did not get smallpox, so he used fluid from
the cowpox blisters to make what became known as a vaccine. Those who received
the cowpox fluid did not get smallpox because they were able to build **antibodies** and
become **immune**.

Worldwide use of the vaccine prevented the spread of smallpox. By 1980 the
World Health Organization (WHO) declared that smallpox was no longer a threat.
Scientists froze the few remaining smallpox **microbes**. They sent them to a few heavily
guarded laboratories around the world. There, scientists can safely study the viruses.

Line count
14
29
40
53
68
82
97
99
112
124
138
150

⚙️ FLUENCY TIP

Practice your phrasing of the second sentence in the second paragraph. Reread it to a
partner, pausing after *cowpox*, *smallpox*, and *blisters*.

Smallpox Comprehension

Read each question. Darken the circle next to the correct answer.

1. How did smallpox get its name?

Ⓐ The germ infected a small group in the population.

Ⓑ The skin was covered in small bumps filled with pus.

Ⓒ The germ infected only small children.

Ⓓ People working with cows got red bumps.

2. What is the smallpox vaccine made of?

Ⓐ fluid from cowpox blisters

Ⓑ fluid from smallpox blisters

Ⓒ fluid from people with smallpox

Ⓓ fluid from cows

3. According to the article, what happened after people received the fluid?

Ⓐ They built up immunity to smallpox.

Ⓑ They built up immunity to cowpox.

Ⓒ They got smallpox.

Ⓓ They got cowpox.

4. What can you conclude from the article?

Ⓐ The smallpox microbe died out on its own.

Ⓑ At one time, many people around the world got the vaccine.

Ⓒ Doctors are worried that a smallpox outbreak will happen soon.

Ⓓ All children in the world are immunized for smallpox.

Answer the question using complete sentences.

5. Why do you think the laboratories holding the smallpox microbes are heavily guarded?

_____

_____

_____

www.harcourtschoolsupply.com
69
Lesson 8: Science to the Rescue
Connecting Reading 7–8, SV 9781419036453

Measles

The measles virus infected more than 90 percent of children before scientists developed a **vaccine** for it. Most victims recover after about ten days. Nevertheless, measles is often fatal to those with **compromised** immune systems and to those who live in famine.

The respiratory system transmits measles, which is highly **contagious**. Sneezing and coughing pass the virus from person to person. Once it infects someone, the disease follows a usual course of high fever, cough, runny nose, and red eyes. Then, after about five days, large, flat, red blotches appear, starting at the hairline. The rash moves steadily down the entire body to the feet.

To combat the disease, the United States licensed the first live vaccine in 1963. After that, measles declined. An outbreak from 1989 to 1991 surprised officials. Research showed that fewer people were being immunized. Since 1993, the United States has reported fewer than 500 measles infections. Now rare in most countries, measles probably can be wiped out through global vaccination.

14
29
43
54
69
86
101
106
121
134
148
163
166

⚙ FLUENCY TIP

Look at the third sentence in the second paragraph. Practice phrasing it with a partner, pausing after *someone, fever, cough, runny nose,* and *red eyes.*

Measles Comprehension

Read each question. Darken the circle next to the correct answer.

1. Who is *most likely* to die from measles?

Ⓐ people who are healthy

Ⓑ people who have poor health

Ⓒ people who have colds

Ⓓ people who have lots of hair

2. What is one way to spread measles?

Ⓐ blood

Ⓑ saliva

Ⓒ nose fluids

Ⓓ tears

3. What happens after a rash starts on the forehead?

Ⓐ People get a fever.

Ⓑ People cough a lot.

Ⓒ People get a rash over the rest of their body.

Ⓓ People lose their hair.

4. What can you conclude from the article?

Ⓐ People in developing countries often get measles.

Ⓑ A vaccine can prevent measles.

Ⓒ Proper hygiene prevents measles.

Ⓓ Measles is a very deadly disease.

Answer the question using complete sentences.

5. Why do you think there were fewer measles infections after 1993?

_____

_____

_____

Lesson 9: The Simple Life
Connecting Background

LEVELED TITLES

- *Consumer Culture — 6.4*
- *Don't Watch . . . Live! — 7.7*
- *Henry David Thoreau — 8.7*

Theme Notes

More and more people are talking about living the simple life. To live simply means to live in harmony with others and the environment. People who do this often change their life. They spend more time with family and friends, buy organic products, and recycle as much as possible. This lesson examines some topics relating to a simple life, including consumer choices, the good and bad of television, and a famous philosopher.

Fluency Focus: Phrasing

Fluent readers pay attention to the phrases, or word groups, in each sentence so that they read faster and more naturally. Chunking, or reading forward through several words at a time, can help readers develop fluency. Punctuation can signal natural pauses and stops. However, readers need to look for groups of words that go together, too.

Fluency Practice

Write this sentence on the board: *Before going to the recycling center, Davis separated the newspapers, cans, plastics, and bottles into different bins.*

Ask partners to rewrite the sentence and use slashes to show the phrasing. Then have them read the words in each word group without pausing.

Comprehension Focus: Making Connections

There are times that a reader will read a story and think, "That's happened to me before," or "This reminds me of another story." The reader is making connections. Linking events or situations often helps with understanding because readers can apply what they know to a new idea. The graphic organizer on page 73 can help students make connections between the main concepts in the articles and their own experiences.

VOCABULARY

- **Consumer Culture**
  attractive
  consumerism
  reject

- **Don't Watch . . . Live!**
  desensitize
  consumers
  reproachable

- **Henry David Thoreau**
  deliberately
  mentor
  philosophy

Name _____ Date _____

Text Connections Graphic Organizer

Topic _____

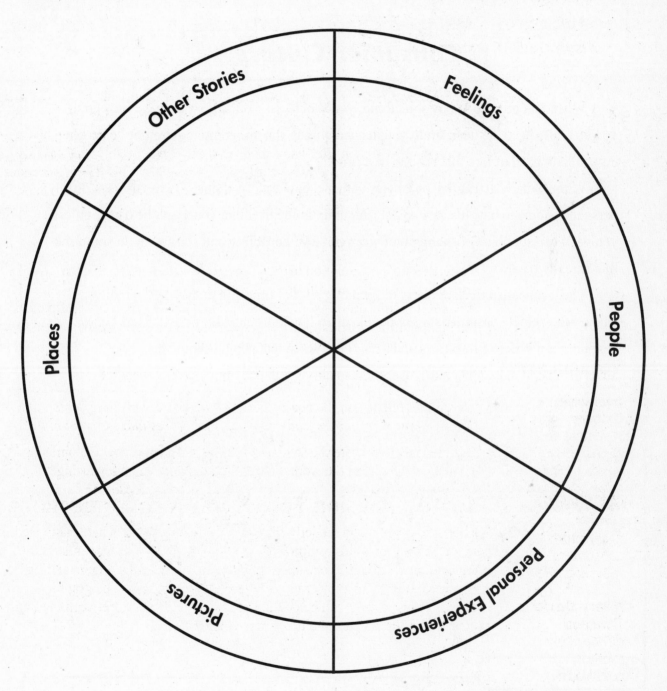

Consumer Culture

	2
When you prepare to buy something, you should ask yourself some questions. First,	15
do you really need the item, or do you just want it? If you are going to purchase something,	34
do you look for the store that has the best price?	45
With so many **attractive** products available, how do you choose? Advertisers skillfully	57
persuade people to buy. It's easy to get caught up in the idea that you won't be happy unless	76
you get a certain brand of shampoo or wear clothes like Hollywood stars'. But do you think	93
this is really true?	97
The term **consumerism** refers to spending a lot of time and money buying things.	111
Those who **reject** consumerism say people often buy more than they need. They believe	125
shopping is a waste of resources and time. They warn that people should be wary of	141
advertising and maintain control over their spending habits by buying only what they	154
really need!	156

⚙ FLUENCY TIP

Look at the third paragraph. Put a slash (/) between each phrase. Now practice your phrasing by rereading the paragraph.

Consumer Culture Comprehension

Read each question. Darken the circle next to the correct answer.

1. According to the article, what should you think about before buying an item?

Ⓐ where it will go once you buy it

Ⓑ when it will be on sale

Ⓒ if it has all the features you want

Ⓓ if it is a want or need

2. How does the author feel about advertising?

Ⓐ It encourages people to buy things they don't need.

Ⓑ It gives true information about products.

Ⓒ It is absolutely necessary.

Ⓓ It makes people unhappy about products.

3. Why do some people oppose consumerism?

Ⓐ They think saving money is a waste of time.

Ⓑ They believe people should buy what they want.

Ⓒ They believe shopping is a waste of time.

Ⓓ The believe people should shop more.

4. Why did the author write this article?

Ⓐ to explain the concept of advertising

Ⓑ to persuade people to become careful shoppers

Ⓒ to make people unhappy about their spending habits

Ⓓ to tell people how to get the best bargains

Answer the question using complete sentences.

5. Do you embrace or reject consumerism? Explain.

_____

_____

_____

Don't Watch . . . Live!

3

   Turn off the TV! Why don't you read a book? Why don't you go out and get some

21

exercise? Do these comments sound familiar?

27

   When the first television sets appeared in the middle of the twentieth century, many

41

people were excited. Television provided entertainment and information. Families gathered

51

around the TV to enjoy programs together. As time went on, television offered a gateway

66

to the world—and beyond. Wars and moon landings came into our living rooms. Images of

82

beautiful, exotic places and foreign cultures introduced us to people and places most could

96

only dream of visiting in person. Today we have immediate access to a world of news and

113

entertainment 24 hours a day.

118

   But with television so readily available, many people worry that we spend too much

132

time watching TV when we could be doing something more worthwhile. Some argue that

146

TV viewing not only wastes time but influences viewers in negative ways. They think

160

programs **desensitize** us to violence. They worry about the advertising on TV. They say

174

the commercials create greedy **consumers** who mistake wants for needs.

184

   What is your opinion of television? Do you think it is a useful machine, or do you think

202

it is **reproachable**?

205

⚙ FLUENCY TIP

Look at the first sentence in the third paragraph. Put a slash (/) between each phrase.
Now practice your phrasing by rereading the paragraph.

Name _____ Date _____

Don't Watch . . . Live! Comprehension

Read each question. Darken the circle next to the correct answer.

1. What does this sentence mean?
"Wars and moon landings came into our living rooms."

Ⓐ People had fights over which television programs to watch.

Ⓑ The moon was an important television topic at one point.

Ⓒ Important but faraway events could be instantly shared with the world.

Ⓓ At one time, people watched television only in the living room.

2. According to the article, what is a negative influence of television?

Ⓐ It makes people buy things.

Ⓑ It makes people dream of exotic places.

Ⓒ It educates people about other cultures.

Ⓓ It shows wars.

3. If something is *reproachable*, what is it?

Ⓐ to be blamed

Ⓑ educational

Ⓒ exciting

Ⓓ uninteresting

4. What can you conclude from the article?

Ⓐ The author watches a lot of television.

Ⓑ Everybody thinks television is a waste of time.

Ⓒ Commercials give useful information.

Ⓓ Some people think there is too much violence on television.

Answer the question using complete sentences.

5. At most, how many hours of TV per day do you think a 14-year-old should watch? Explain.

_____

_____

_____

Henry David Thoreau

	3

Mention the name *Walden*, and many people think of one of the best-known **16**
experiments in simple living in American history. From 1845 to 1847, Henry David Thoreau **30**
lived in a small cabin in the woods next to a Massachusetts pond. Thoreau wrote a book **47**
about his experience and named it *Walden*, after the pond. Explaining his decision, Thoreau **61**
writes, "I went to the woods because I wished to live **deliberately**, to front only the essential **78**
facts of life, and to see if I could not learn what it had to teach, and not, when I came to die, **101**
discover that I had not lived. I wanted to live deep and suck all the marrow of life." Thoreau **120**
grew beans, picked wild berries, studied nature, but most of all, spent time writing. Living **135**
simply allowed Thoreau time to pursue the activity he liked best. **146**

Although Thoreau lived alone, he was not a hermit. Sometimes friends came to visit, **160**
or he walked two miles to a neighboring town to visit them. One friend, Ralph Waldo **176**
Emerson, served as Thoreau's **mentor**. He and Thoreau wrote about their ideas, emphasizing **189**
the individual, nature, emotion, intuition, and the spirit. Their **philosophy** is known as **202**
Transcendentalism. **203**

 FLUENCY TIP

Practice phrasing the quotation from *Walden*, pausing at commas.

Henry David Thoreau Comprehension

Read each question. Darken the circle next to the correct answer.

1. What was the title of Thoreau's book?

Ⓐ *Thoreau*

Ⓑ *Simple Living*

Ⓒ *Walden*

Ⓓ *Transcendentalism*

2. What does Thoreau mean when he says, "I wished to live deliberately"?

Ⓐ He wanted to be left alone in nature.

Ⓑ He wanted to think about and reflect on his daily life.

Ⓒ He wanted to learn about nature and write about it.

Ⓓ He wanted to grow organic food to share with others.

3. What did Thoreau like to do best?

Ⓐ garden

Ⓑ walk

Ⓒ write

Ⓓ talk with friends

4. As a mentor, what did Ralph Waldo Emerson most likely do?

Ⓐ encourage Thoreau's ideas

Ⓑ help Thoreau in the garden

Ⓒ give Thoreau paper and pen to write with

Ⓓ bring Thoreau books to read

Answer the questions using complete sentences.

5. If you had to give up one item in an effort to live more simply, what would it be? Why?

_____

_____

_____

Lesson 10: Technology for Living
Connecting Background

Theme Notes

Technology is a part of our daily lives. It keeps us entertained, helps us communicate, and makes chores easy. Most inventions are the result of someone seeing a problem and trying to find a solution. Others are simply accidents, discovered when a scientist is working on something else. The articles in this lesson explore some of the most popular inventions: the telephone, television, and microwave.

Fluency Focus: Punctuation

Fluent readers pay attention to punctuation to help themselves understand and remember what they read. They pause at commas and stop briefly at periods, ellipses, and dashes. A question mark or exclamation point signals they should change their voice. Following these clues will break a long sentence into smaller, more understandable parts.

Fluency Practice

Write this sentence on the board: *I am glad that technology, which has come such a long way in the last fifty years, has given us many products we use every day: television—both HD and cable—microwave ovens, and computers.*

Invite partners to alternate reading the sentence, paying attention to the punctuation cues.

Comprehension Focus: Problem and Solution

Scientists solve problems. They think about something that can be improved and find a way to make it better. In some science articles, the problem may not be clearly explained, but the solution is often described in detail. The Problem and Solution Charts on page 81 will help students identify the problems some scientists solved.

Problem and Solution Charts

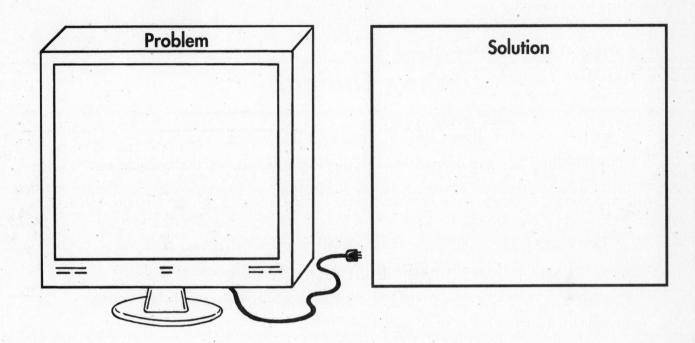

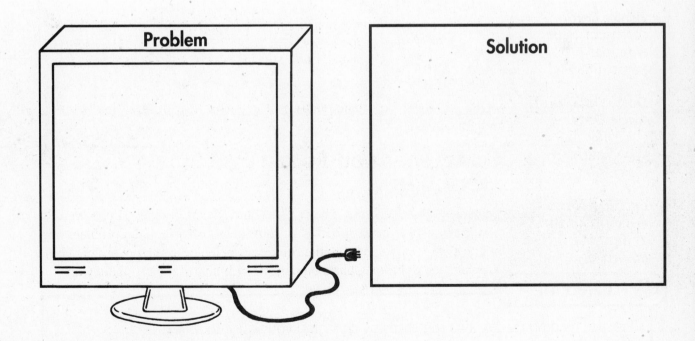

81

Lesson 10: Technology for Living
Connecting Reading 7–8, SV 9781419036453

Who's Calling?

    In 1876 Alexander Graham Bell's new invention, the telephone, changed **communication**. People could speak to each other over a distance—if that distance was wired for the phones. Now we can call almost anywhere at almost any time with cell phones.

    How are these phones different from those early phones? Cell phones are actually radios. They pick up signals from **antennas**. When cell phones first came out, there was one antenna in each city. Each antenna had about 25 channels. When you dialed, your call was connected through one of those channels.

    Cellular companies have changed this process. Now each city has many different cells. The cells cover **approximately** ten miles. Each cell also has its own tower and radio equipment, which allows it to send and receive signals over 1,500 channels! What will come next?

12
26
42
43
56
71
87
94
106
122
136
138

⚙️ FLUENCY TIP

Practice reading the last two sentences by changing your voice to reflect the punctuation.

Who's Calling? Comprehension

Read each question. Darken the circle next to the correct answer.

1. What is the most recent phone discussed in the article?

Ⓐ wired phone

Ⓑ cell phone

Ⓒ digital phone

Ⓓ analog phone

2. What problem did Alexander Graham Bell solve?

Ⓐ People could not communicate over a long distance.

Ⓑ People did not have telephones in the house.

Ⓒ Radio and telephone signals interrupted each other.

Ⓓ Wires didn't carry sounds far enough.

3. How were the first phones different from cell phones?

Ⓐ The first phones used radio waves.

Ⓑ The first phones needed antennas.

Ⓒ The first phones covered only ten miles.

Ⓓ The first phones used wires.

4. With the growing number of towers, what can you conclude?

Ⓐ Cities competed to have the greatest number of towers.

Ⓑ Taller towers worked better.

Ⓒ One tower was not enough for the growing number of cell phone users.

Ⓓ The company that had the most towers got to sell more cell phones.

Answer the question using complete sentences.

5. What might the phones of the future be like?

_____

_____

_____

Dots, Dots, and More Dots

5

Have you ever seen paintings where the artists make pictures with closely spaced | 18

dots, rather than solid areas of color? When the dots are close together and you stand | 34

far enough away, the dots seem to merge into one picture. Scientists used this idea to | 50

develop technology to send pictures **electronically**. That's what TVs and computers do. | 62

Row by row, they **systematically** break images into thousands of tiny dots. The dots are | 77

called *pixels*, short for *picture elements*. The pixels travel through the air or cable to your | 93

TV's antenna, satellite dish, or cable box, where the receiver **reassembles** them. | 105

We can also divide a moving scene into a group of still pictures. If we show the | 122

still pictures in order very quickly, our brains fuse them back into one moving scene. If | 138

we don't like what we're seeing, our brains can control that, too—by letting us change | 154

the channel! | 156

⚙ FLUENCY TIP

When you read the last sentence, pause briefly at commas and a little longer at
the dash.

---

www.harcourtschoolsupply.com
84
Lesson 10: Technology for Living
Connecting Reading 7–8, SV 9781419036453

Dots, Dots, and More Dots Comprehension

Read each question. Darken the circle next to the correct answer.

1. What are the dots that make up the pictures in the computer called?

Ⓐ systems

Ⓑ elements

Ⓒ electronics

Ⓓ pixels

2. What problem did scientists solve with the dot pictures?

Ⓐ sending pictures electronically

Ⓑ using paint to create pictures

Ⓒ making movies

Ⓓ helping the brain see

3. What happens after the dots travel through the air?

Ⓐ The computer breaks the picture into dots.

Ⓑ An antenna receives the dot pictures.

Ⓒ A receiver captures the dot pictures.

Ⓓ A satellite dish reassembles the pictures.

4. What helps people see movies?

Ⓐ the brain

Ⓑ dot pictures

Ⓒ paintings

Ⓓ picture elements

Answer the question using complete sentences.

5. In what other ways might the technology of television be used?

_____

_____

_____

Lesson 10: Technology for Living
Connecting Reading 7–8, SV 9781419036453

Exciting News

One day in 1946, inventor Percy Spencer was working on a machine that used high-frequency **electromagnetic** radio waves. He noticed that a candy bar that he had in his pocket started to melt. Curious, he grabbed a bag of unpopped popcorn and held it in front of the machine. Amazingly, the kernels popped! The waves were microwaves, a type of radio wave, and his **impromptu** experiment led him to invent the microwave oven.

These high-frequency electromagnetic waves are **absorbed** by water, fats, and sugars—substances that are contained in most foods. As the waves are absorbed, they excite the molecules in the food, creating heat that cooks the food. Because of this, a microwave oven cooks food quickly. The waves, however, are not absorbed by materials such as plastics, glass, or ceramics. This allows these materials to be used as containers for the food. Metal blocks and repels microwaves, which is why you can't put metal into the microwave oven.

So when you go home today, excite some molecules in your favorite snack and enjoy!

2
17
31
48
62
75
85
99
115
128
144
160
162
177

 FLUENCY TIP

Pause briefly at commas and a little longer at the dash, and stop briefly at periods and exclamation points.

Exciting News Comprehension

Read each question. Darken the circle next to the correct answer.

1. What first made Spencer notice that electromagnetic waves could cook food?

Ⓐ He popped some popcorn.

Ⓑ A candy bar started melting.

Ⓒ The plastic got soft.

Ⓓ Some metal began to spark.

2. What are microwaves?

Ⓐ sound waves

Ⓑ radio waves

Ⓒ electric waves

Ⓓ water waves

3. What happens after the waves are absorbed by food?

Ⓐ They enter the food through fats, water, and sugars.

Ⓑ They cool molecules.

Ⓒ They excite molecules.

Ⓓ They are absorbed by containers.

4. What problem did Spencer solve?

Ⓐ how to keep plastic containers from melting

Ⓑ how to use metal in microwave ovens

Ⓒ how to cook food quickly

Ⓓ how to pop popcorn using heat

Answer the question using complete sentences.

5. How would life be different for you if you did not have a microwave oven?

_____

_____

_____

Lesson 11: Save Us from Ourselves!

Connecting Background

- *Water for Thought* — 6.6
- *Huge and Growing* — 7.8
- *What's in Your Breath?* — 8.9

Theme Notes

Understanding Earth's environmental problems is not simple. There are often many factors that create one problem. The effect or effects can be devastating. In this lesson, readers will learn about several problems facing the environment, their causes and effects, and how people can work together to solve them. The problems cover ground water, electronic wastes, and air quality.

Fluency Focus: Word Accuracy

When reading with accuracy, fluent readers read each word part and blend it smoothly together. They learn how to pronounce difficult words and what the words mean. They do not skip or add words. Fluent readers often look for a prefix, suffix, or familiar word part to help them figure out a word and its meaning. They also use a dictionary.

Fluency Practice

Write this sentence on the board: *When Anna discussed nonpoint-source pollution, she raised some very good points.*

Challenge partners to discuss familiar words and word parts in *nonpoint-source* before they practice reading the sentence.

Comprehension Focus: Cause and Effect

A cause is a reason that something happens, while an effect is the result of the cause. Science is full of cause and effect relationships. Sometimes one cause can have more than one effect. Conversely, several causes can result in one effect. Scientists often explain these occurrences and events to help people understand the relationships. The Cause and Effect Charts on page 89 can help students identify the relationships in the articles.

VOCABULARY

- *Water for Thought*
  statistics
  precious
  nonpoint-source
    pollution

- *Huge and Growing*
  discarded
  rapidly
  inhabitants

- *What's in Your Breath?*
  dissipate
  emissions
  eliminate

Name _____ Date _____

Cause and Effect Charts

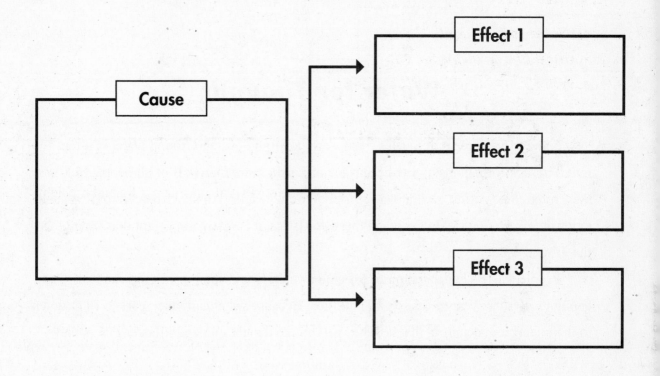

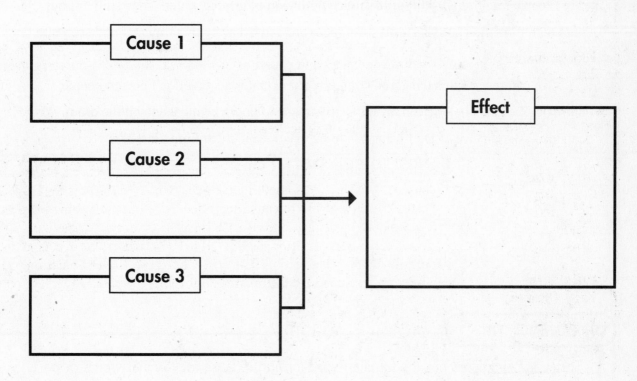

Connecting Reading 7–8, SV 9781419036453

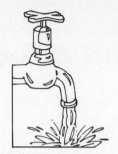

Water for Thought

3

16
32
48
64
67
81
99
117
119
131
144
146
160
177
191

Ninety-five percent of Earth's fresh water is ground water. Ground water is often found in rock formations under the surface of Earth. More than half of all people in the United States drink ground water from their own wells. About 81 percent of town and city water is ground water. Based on these **statistics**, it is really important that we protect the ground water!

People waste a huge amount of **precious** water. One dripping sink tap can leak enough water in a year to fill up two bathtubs. Because water can take years to filter down to the underground aquifer that holds it, we run the danger of using it faster than it can be replaced.

People often cause **nonpoint-source pollution** of ground water. They spill or pour out contaminants. These harmful substances are carried away by rainwater and seep into the ground.

We can reverse this dangerous trend by using materials that don't poison people or animals. We can stop or clean up spills and refuse to pour chemicals down the drain. We can also ask ourselves, "Do I want this to be in someone's drinking glass?"

⚙ FLUENCY TIP

The word *formations* has the familiar word *form* in it. Look for familiar words or parts within new words.

Name _____ Date _____

Water for Thought Comprehension

Read each question. Darken the circle next to the correct answer.

1. Why is ground water important to the United States?

   Ⓐ It is the main source of drinking water for many people.

   Ⓑ Water provides the country's main source of power.

   Ⓒ It keeps the ground wet for healthy crop growth.

   Ⓓ It keeps rivers and lakes full.

2. What does *precious* mean in this sentence?
"People waste a huge amount of precious water."

   Ⓐ cute

   Ⓑ little

   Ⓒ valuable

   Ⓓ not available

3. What can you conclude from the article?

   Ⓐ People are probably drinking contaminated water.

   Ⓑ Many people are working to stop nonpoint-source pollution.

   Ⓒ The aquifer is very low.

   Ⓓ People don't care about water pollution.

4. According to the article, what is one cause of water pollution?

   Ⓐ People use materials that are not poisonous.

   Ⓑ People are pouring chemicals down the drain.

   Ⓒ Rainwater is used as drinking water.

   Ⓓ People take out too much ground water.

Answer the questions using complete sentences.

5. What response did you have to this article? Will it impact your behavior at home or in the environment? Explain.

_____

_____

_____

Lesson 11: Save Us from Ourselves!
Connecting Reading 7–8, SV 9781419036453

Huge and Growing

3

Many people don't know what North America's fastest growing source of waste is. | 16

It didn't exist twenty years ago. It is electronic waste, also called *e-waste*. E-waste includes | 31

old computer systems, TVs, and cell phones. About six million pounds of electronics are | 45

discarded in the United States every day. | 52

Computer systems are an example of growing e-waste. **Rapidly** changing technology | 63

that provides faster, more powerful machines means that people buy new equipment. Old | 76

computer systems sit in closets, offices, and landfills. Each one has dangerous materials | 89

in it. If the fluids leak, they can get into soil or water and make people sick! | 106

What helps to fight e-waste? People can repair broken computers so they work better. | 120

They might donate working electronics to people who need them. Some cities, counties, | 133

and businesses also recycle old electronics. No one needs poisons just sitting in a closet! | 148

It is best for the environment and its **inhabitants** when people properly dispose of their | 163

e-waste. | 164

⚙ FLUENCY TIP

Two vowels together usually make only one sound. Keep vowel pairs together as you read the syllables of *counties* and *poisons*.

Huge and Growing Comprehension

Read each question. Darken the circle next to the correct answer.

1. What is *e-waste*?

Ⓐ discarded electronics

Ⓑ old electronic mail

Ⓒ new computers

Ⓓ time wasted on the computer

2. Why is e-waste dangerous?

Ⓐ Computers may leak harmful fluids.

Ⓑ It makes computers slow.

Ⓒ People neglect other responsibilities.

Ⓓ People use computers with harmful fluids.

3. According to the article, what is one bad effect of changing technology?

Ⓐ The newest technology is dangerous.

Ⓑ The new systems don't always work.

Ⓒ Old systems are not discarded properly.

Ⓓ People spend too much money buying the new systems.

4. Which sentence from the article states an opinion?

Ⓐ About six million pounds of electronics are discarded in the United States every day.

Ⓑ Old computer systems sit in closets, offices, and landfills.

Ⓒ No one needs poisons just sitting in a closet!

Ⓓ People can repair broken computers so they work better.

Answer the question using complete sentences.

5. How will this article influence your attitude about and behavior toward computer systems?

_____

_____

_____

What's in Your Breath?

Each person takes over 20,000 breaths daily, inhaling up to 35 gallons of air necessary | 4
for survival. Unfortunately, that air is often polluted. People's activities often release | 19
greenhouse gases, dust, and molds into the air. It takes years for gases circling above to | 31
reach Earth's outer atmosphere and **dissipate**. Scientists can only predict how air pollution | 47
from manufacturing and vehicle **emissions** will impact future life on Earth. | 60

Ozone is a good gas when it's where it should be, which is in a layer about 10 to 30 | 71
miles above Earth. The ozone layer acts as a barrier that screens out harmful light rays. | 91
However, near Earth's surface, ozone is destructive and damages plants and our bodies, | 107
especially the lungs and eyes. Other gases from human activities further reduce the good | 120
ozone layer, resulting in the formation of additional bad ozone. | 134

Most adults and many teens spend about 90 percent of their time indoors. So is it safer | 144
to remain indoors and breathe that air? Actually, air quality can be worse in tightly sealed | 161
buildings and can cause just as much damage! | 177

So what is the answer to this growing ozone problem? Wherever people are, they | 185
would be wise to reduce the amount of emissions as much as possible. They should also | 199
eliminate smoke and chemical sprays and keep homes free of dust and mold. | 215

Line counts at right: 4, 19, 31, 47, 60, 71, 91, 107, 120, 134, 144, 161, 177, 185, 199, 215, 228

⚙ FLUENCY TIP

In the word *unfortunately*, you may notice *fortune*, minus the e. Often, looking for a familiar word will help you decode an unfamiliar word.

Name _____ Date _____

What's in Your Breath? Comprehension

Read each question. Darken the circle next to the correct answer.

1. What is this article mostly about?

Ⓐ the ozone layer

Ⓑ the substances in the air people breathe

Ⓒ kinds of pollution

Ⓓ how to get rid of pollution

2. What is one reason that scientists can't predict how manufacturing and car emissions will impact future life?

Ⓐ It is a recent problem, so they are in the process of researching the effects.

Ⓑ The pollutants haven't had time to dissipate.

Ⓒ They are waiting to see what people will be doing in the future.

Ⓓ People spend too much time indoors, so scientists can't collect accurate data.

3. Which of the following could be an air pollutant?

Ⓐ indoor plants

Ⓑ apples

Ⓒ clothes dryers

Ⓓ hair spray

4. What can you conclude about the author?

Ⓐ The author has a very clean house.

Ⓑ The author reduces vehicle emissions.

Ⓒ The author is concerned about the environment.

Ⓓ The author is a scientist.

Answer the question using complete sentences.

5. What can you do to reduce pollution inside your home?

_____

_____

_____

Lesson 11: Save Us from Ourselves!
Connecting Reading 7–8, SV 9781419036453

Lesson 12: How Great Is Art!
Connecting Background

LEVELED TITLES

- *Public Murals — 6.8*
- *Anime — 8.0*
- *The Political Cartoon — 9.0*

Theme Notes

When people think of art, they often visualize paintings. However, art is all around us. It can be found in statues, collages, furniture, and the shapes of buildings. This lesson highlights other kinds of art, including murals, Japanese cartoons, and political cartoons.

Fluency Focus: Word Accuracy

To read fluently and smoothly, readers need to say words accurately. Fluent readers learn all the words in a selection. They learn how to pronounce them and what the words mean. They look in advance for difficult words, especially names of people and place names. Then they sound out each unfamiliar word as they read and think about whether its meaning makes sense. Good readers use a dictionary if they need additional help.

Fluency Practice

Write these sentences on the board:

- *Through I enjoy painting with watercolors, I prefer acrylics.*
- *The paintings were limed up on the wall.*
- *What do you think of that the artist?*

Have partners rewrite the sentences without the mistakes and read them fluently.

Comprehension Focus: Summarizing

When readers summarize, they retell the main points of what they have learned. They take a large piece of text and condense it into just the essential facts. They don't include lots of details. They include only the critical details that support the main ideas. The Summarizing Notes graphic organizer on page 97 can help students identify the important information in each paragraph of the text.

VOCABULARY

- **Public Murals**
  unique
  annoying
  zeal

- **Anime**
  innovative
  ultracute
  confusion

- **The Political Cartoon**
  subjective
  objective
  criticism

Summarizing Notes

Paragraph 1 _____

_____

_____

Paragraph 2 _____

_____

_____

Paragraph 3 _____

_____

_____

Paragraph 4 _____

_____

_____

Article Summary _____

_____

_____

Public Murals

	2
Public murals are popping up in plain sight—under bridges, on walls, along city	16
streets! Art is coming out into the open, no longer hidden in a museum or art gallery.	33
These murals bring a community together, allowing people to express what is	45
important to them. Murals also show what makes the neighborhood **unique** and what the	59
residents value. The best part is that murals replace **annoying** graffiti!	70
Murals also bring neighbors and artists together. First, the group must decide on a site.	85
Next, they work hand in hand to develop their ideas. Some people may even be asked to	102
serve as models or to offer to store supplies in their homes. Then artists and volunteers of	119
all ages work with **zeal** to paint the murals.	128
Public murals educate both children and adults. They join neighbors and artists in a	142
common goal and allow many people to be exposed to fine art. Finally, murals bring pride	158
to neighborhoods.	160

Public murals are popping up in plain sight—under bridges, on walls, along city streets! Art is coming out into the open, no longer hidden in a museum or art gallery.

These murals bring a community together, allowing people to express what is important to them. Murals also show what makes the neighborhood **unique** and what the residents value. The best part is that murals replace **annoying** graffiti!

Murals also bring neighbors and artists together. First, the group must decide on a site. Next, they work hand in hand to develop their ideas. Some people may even be asked to serve as models or to offer to store supplies in their homes. Then artists and volunteers of all ages work with **zeal** to paint the murals.

Public murals educate both children and adults. They join neighbors and artists in a common goal and allow many people to be exposed to fine art. Finally, murals bring pride to neighborhoods.

⚙ FLUENCY TIP

The second paragraph has some hard words, such as *unique* and *annoying*. Read them carefully so you don't say the wrong word.

Public Murals Comprehension

Read each question. Darken the circle next to the correct answer.

1. What does the author mean when she says, "Art is coming out into the open"?

Ⓐ More art museums are opening around the country.

Ⓑ Galleries are staying open longer hours.

Ⓒ Artists are showing their murals in public areas.

Ⓓ People are discovering that bridges are a form of art.

2. According to the article, in what way is a mural a good thing?

Ⓐ It is large, so it can be easily seen.

Ⓑ It represents the values of the community.

Ⓒ It allows a starving artist to work.

Ⓓ It encourages people to visit a museum.

3. What can happen while a mural is being painted?

Ⓐ Community members might store the artist's supplies.

Ⓑ People choose a site.

Ⓒ The community has a party to unveil the mural.

Ⓓ The community and artist brainstorm ideas.

4. How might an artist show *zeal*?

Ⓐ by painting only the important elements

Ⓑ by completing the project very slowly

Ⓒ by allowing no one to help

Ⓓ by working with enthusiasm

Answer the questions using complete sentences.

5. What kind of mural would you suggest for your school? Why?

_____

_____

_____

Anime

1

15

30

43

59

62

75

91

106

117

132

147

160

Do you enjoy watching cartoons? Well, *anime** is a name for Japanese cartoons that appear in TV series, movies, and videos. Many of these **innovative** cartoons have a clean, colorful look with **ultracute** characters. Moreover, they often deal with current issues, such as the environment and the role of robots, in a fantasy world filled with aliens, superheroes, and space vehicles.

But the differences between Japanese and U.S. cultures can lead to **confusion**. For example, large eyes are a common feature of anime characters. We see these eyes as simply cute. In Japan these wide eyes are a way to see how a character feels.

Anime targets a wide audience—not just children. Traditional children's cartoons present a world of funny animals and fairy-tale characters, such as Mickey Mouse and Snow White. Anime crosses the divide between children and adults. It revs things up with action, crime, science fiction, and romance, so there is something for just about everyone!

*(AN ih may)

 **FLUENCY TIP**

Before you read, look for any difficult words and be sure you can say them. Then you'll be able to read without errors.

Lesson 12: How Great Is Art!
Connecting Reading 7–8, SV 9781419036453

Anime Comprehension

Read each question. Darken the circle next to the correct answer.

1. In which genre do most anime cartoons belong?

Ⓐ biography

Ⓑ mystery

Ⓒ science fiction

Ⓓ folklore

2. How is Japanese anime different from U.S. cartoons?

Ⓐ The characters' eyes show expression.

Ⓑ The cartoons show robots.

Ⓒ The themes deal with environmental issues.

Ⓓ Some characters are superheroes.

3. Why might adults like anime?

Ⓐ The plots have action and romance.

Ⓑ Familiar U.S. cartoon characters are shown in some anime.

Ⓒ The cartoons have a clean, colorful look.

Ⓓ They can get the videos in stores.

4. Why might anime be considered innovative?

Ⓐ It deals with current issues.

Ⓑ It is made into movies.

Ⓒ The characters have big eyes.

Ⓓ Adults like to watch these cartoons.

Answer the question using complete sentences.

5. Is anime a good thing? Explain.

_____

_____

_____

The Political Cartoon

3

19

31

39

51

65

82

95

110

120

137

153

166

179

The political cartoon is a picture or comic strip with a message. It offers a **subjective** comment about current event issues, rather than **objective** news. Often these cartoons appear on the editorial page of a newspaper.

Cartoonists present thoughts as humorous art. They often use caricature, a drawing that exaggerates the characteristics of someone or something. In the world of caricature, a big nose grows to the size of a large pickle, or a long neck attains skyscraper proportions.

Cartoonists may also use common symbols in their cartoons. Uncle Sam may represent the United States, or a donkey may represent the Democratic Party. In this way, political cartoons become metaphors, with one thing used to represent another.

The political cartoon often is a way of poking fun at those in power. It reflects a specific point of view and has a purpose beyond the chuckle. But when does a political cartoon cross the line? When does **criticism**, even when humorous, become unfair? Perhaps the measure of fairness becomes this: Does the cartoon target an essential truth?

⚙ FLUENCY TIP

Sound out each part of long words such as *political, editorial, criticism,* or *caricature.* Then blend the sounds. If you need help, consult a dictionary.

Connecting Reading 7–8, SV 9781419036453

The Political Cartoon Comprehension

Read each question. Darken the circle next to the correct answer.

1. What is the purpose of a political cartoon?

Ⓐ It helps people make a decision about an important issue.

Ⓑ It gives facts about a political issue.

Ⓒ It explains symbols representing the government.

Ⓓ It sends a message about a current event.

2. Why are political cartoons subjective?

Ⓐ They represent the artist's opinion.

Ⓑ They explain truths in the government.

Ⓒ An artist signs them.

Ⓓ They relate only facts about current events.

3. In a political cartoon, what might the Statue of Liberty represent?

Ⓐ the president

Ⓑ the United States

Ⓒ factory owners

Ⓓ statues in a museum

4. How might a political cartoon be unfair?

Ⓐ when it exaggerates someone's features

Ⓑ when it uses symbols

Ⓒ when it targets something that is not true

Ⓓ when it makes people laugh

Answer the questions using complete sentences.

5. Find a political cartoon. What current event does it show? What does it show about the artist? Do you agree or disagree? Explain.

_____

_____

_____

Lesson 13: Cityscapes
Connecting Background

LEVELED TITLES

- *At the Water's Edge* — 6.8
- *The Paris of the South* — 8.1
- *The City Different* — 9.2

Theme Notes

A city is a busy place. People work and live in high-rise buildings. Various transportation options move people from place to place. And often, food and entertainment businesses stay open until early in the morning. This lesson looks at three U.S. cities—Bellingham, Washington; Asheville, North Carolina; and Santa Fe, New Mexico.

Fluency Focus: Phrasing

Phrasing is an important aspect of fluent reading. When someone reads word-for-word, the text does not sound natural. It is important to read in phrases, or natural chunks. Sometimes, punctuation can help readers phrase correctly. They should try chunking the text to make the sentence sound like natural speech.

Fluency Practice

Write this sentence on the board: *My great-aunt lives in Venice, an Italian city famous for its beautiful canals.*

Have partners practice the sentence, chunking it in different ways. Ask them to determine which sounds most like natural speech.

Comprehension Focus: Making Inferences

Writers don't always tell everything they want readers to understand about a story. Sometimes readers have to figure something out from hints the author provides in the text. This is called making an inference. Good readers think about the hints and clues that the author is giving as they read. The Making Inferences Graphic Organizer on page 105 can help readers read actively for clues.

VOCABULARY

- *At the Water's Edge*
  diverse
  inhabitants
  thrive

- *The Paris of the South*
  diverse
  exemplify
  originated

- *The City Different*
  appropriately
  diverse
  intrigued

Making Inferences Graphic Organizer

Title _____

What the Text Says in Your Own Words

Quotation

Reasoning

What the Text Says in Your Own Words

Quotation

Reasoning

Name _____   Date _____

At the Water's Edge

	4
Bellingham, Washington, sits by water. Here three rivers flow into a bay. Bellingham	17
is the last major city before the West Coast meets Canada.	28
Bellingham's location offers **diverse** natural resources. Native Americans fished the	38
local waters for centuries. Other people settled here because of the area's wood and coal.	53
Sea and water travel were important to the **inhabitants**, too. They could easily receive	67
supplies. Businesses could ship things to others just as easily.	77
Today, many businesses **thrive** in Bellingham and help it grow. People move here	90
to get away from large, crowded cities and bad air. The sea and water travel are still very	108
important. Bellingham's port is busy with hundreds of boats. Some boats take people to	122
watch whales. Ships carry people and cars to islands or to Alaska. In addition, the citizens	138
can enjoy the city's beautiful trails and parks. On some days, they even see steam rising	154
from Mount Baker, an active volcano.	160

⚙ FLUENCY TIP

A city name and its state name have a comma between them. Read the names together instead of pausing.

Lesson 13: Cityscapes
Connecting Reading 7–8, SV 9781419036453

At the Water's Edge Comprehension

Read each question. Darken the circle next to the correct answer.

1. Where is Bellingham located?

Ⓐ in the northwest part of the United States

Ⓑ on the west coast of Canada

Ⓒ on the east coast of the United States

Ⓓ in Washington, D.C.

2. What resources drew settlers to Bellingham?

Ⓐ water and wool

Ⓑ cities and businesses

Ⓒ gold and fish

Ⓓ coal and wood

3. How did its location next to water help Bellingham's early development?

Ⓐ Tourists liked to come to fish.

Ⓑ People could swim all year long in the bay.

Ⓒ The ocean brought fresh, clean air.

Ⓓ People could easily receive supplies by water.

4. What can you conclude about Bellingham?

Ⓐ Wood is still an important resource for Bellingham.

Ⓑ The volcano will explode soon.

Ⓒ There are many outdoor activities for people to enjoy.

Ⓓ The city has many tall buildings filled with people.

Answer the question using complete sentences.

5. Would Bellingham be a major city if people could not use the port? Explain.

_____

_____

_____

The Paris of the South

	5

Asheville, North Carolina, lies in a natural bowl in the Blue Ridge Mountains. Great   19
Smoky Mountain National Park sits to the west. The city is an economic and cultural center   35
for the western third of the state.   42

Native Americans lived in the forested area for centuries. Later, Scotch-Irish   53
immigrants and slaves settled there. The city continued to grow through the years. People   67
and their animals could travel through the mountains or along a river and stop in Asheville.   83
Asheville became known for health resorts and outdoor fun.   92

Asheville's natural beauty has attracted **diverse** artists. A large, old house and several   105
downtown buildings **exemplify** famous designs. The city has theaters for plays and galleries   118
to exhibit paintings. A trail of sculptures weaves through downtown. People share other   131
cultural arts that **originated** in the Southern mountains, including lively old-time music,   143
dances, and crafts, so they will not be forgotten. This emphasis on art has given Asheville   159
the name "Paris of the South."   165

⚙ FLUENCY TIP

Proper phrasing sounds natural. Practice phrasing the last sentence: "This emphasis on art / has given Asheville the name / 'Paris of the South.'"

The Paris of the South Comprehension

Read each question. Darken the circle next to the correct answer.

1. How is Asheville a diverse city?

Ⓐ It is in the Blue Ridge Mountains.

Ⓑ Native Americans were the original inhabitants.

Ⓒ It showcases examples of old and new art today.

Ⓓ It has many health resorts.

2. Who came to Asheville after the Scotch-Irish immigrants?

Ⓐ slaves

Ⓑ Native Americans

Ⓒ people traveling through the mountains

Ⓓ French explorers

3. What can you conclude about Asheville?

Ⓐ People support the arts by going to many different events.

Ⓑ It no longer has health resorts.

Ⓒ It is close to Paris.

Ⓓ Most of the downtown buildings are old.

4. What can you infer about the art in Paris?

Ⓐ There is a large variety of art in Paris.

Ⓑ Paris has old-time music, too.

Ⓒ People don't like dancing in Paris.

Ⓓ It does not have as much art as Asheville.

Answer the questions using complete sentences.

5. If you went to Asheville, what might you like to do? Why?

_____

_____

_____

The City Different

| | 3 |

For residents and visitors, the motto "The City Different" **appropriately** describes a | 15

place that shows three **diverse** cultures. This desert city is the busy, but low-stress, state | 30

capital of New Mexico, and its name is Santa Fe. | 40

When the Spanish built Santa Fe, making it the colonial capital in 1610, Native | 54

Americans had already lived there for centuries. More people came to the city on a trading | 70

road from Mexico City. Next, Santa Fe was the capital of the New Mexico Territory, owned | 86

first by Mexico and then the United States. "Anglos," people of non-Hispanic European | 99

descent, came on the Santa Fe Trail. As a result of all these influences, the state capital | 116

today has strong Native American, Hispanic, and Anglo cultures. People live, build, and | 129

celebrate with a mix of these cultures and new ideas. | 139

Santa Fe's beautiful desert setting has **intrigued** many artists. They have helped the | 152

city become a world center of art. | 159

Like the original inhabitants, the new residents use the resources found in the area. | 173

A growing number of people and businesses use sunlight for power. Builders use earth | 187

materials to make many new buildings. Santa Fe is both very old and very new. | 202

⚙️ FLUENCY TIP

The second sentence in the first paragraph is long. Use the commas to help you phrase it.

The City Different Comprehension

Read each question. Darken the circle next to the correct answer.

1. Who were the second inhabitants of Santa Fe?

Ⓐ Europeans

Ⓑ French

Ⓒ Native Americans

Ⓓ Spanish

2. When was Santa Fe the capital of the New Mexico Territory?

Ⓐ before becoming the Spanish colonial capital

Ⓑ before the Native Americans lived there

Ⓒ when people traveled on the trading road from Mexico

Ⓓ when Anglos traveled on the Santa Fe Trail

3. Which nationality would be considered Anglo?

Ⓐ Portuguese

Ⓑ Spanish

Ⓒ Italian

Ⓓ Mexican

4. Why is Santa Fe a good location for people interested in using sunlight for power?

Ⓐ The city is close to the sun.

Ⓑ The city is in the desert.

Ⓒ The city offers rebates for places with solar power.

Ⓓ The sun never sets during parts of the year.

Answer the question using complete sentences.

5. What is another motto that could appropriately describe Santa Fe?

_____

_____

_____

Lesson 14: Pursuit of Peace
Connecting Background

Theme Notes

Conflicts are struggles that people face. A conflict can be internal, in which people deal with personal issues, or external, in which two or more people disagree. Even in the midst of these situations, there are people who attempt to be the peacemakers. The readings in this lesson highlight Alfred Nobel and two organizations that are true peacemakers.

Fluency Focus: Expression

Fluent readers read with expression, or feeling. They think about the meaning of the text and then use the tone and rhythm of their voice to communicate that meaning. Sometimes, punctuation gives clues about the way a sentence should be read. However, other information can give hints, too. Dialogue should be read based on what the characters are like and what they might be feeling at that point in the story.

Fluency Practice

Write these sentences on the board:

- *I am going to get an award at the next school assembly!*
- *The movie about Alfred Nobel was good—very good.*
- *The upset woman said in a frustrated voice, "That person just cut in front of me!"*

Discuss the clues to determine the expression. Then have partners read the sentences.

Comprehension Focus: Monitoring Comprehension

When fluent readers monitor their comprehension, they pause to think. They ask themselves questions such as "Does this make sense? Could I explain what I read?" They will reread a sentence or paragraph if they don't understand. The chart on page 113 can help students establish a plan for monitoring comprehension.

VOCABULARY

- **Nobel Peace Prize**
  explosives
  tragically
  controversy

- **Jody Williams and the ICBL**
  artificial
  previous
  dispute

- **Doctors Without Borders**
  administrators
  disputes
  influence

Name _____ Date _____

Monitoring Comprehension Chart

Sentence or Word I Don't Understand	What I Think It Means	How I Can Find Out	What the Sentence or Word Means

Nobel Peace Prize

3
16
30
46
48
61
77
89
96
110
126
143
147

Alfred Nobel was born in 1833 in Sweden. His father manufactured simple **explosives** for construction use. Nobel followed in his father's footsteps. He thought that people needed a safe way to blast away rock to build roads, tunnels, and canals. So Nobel experimented with explosives.

Tragically, Nobel's lab blew up during an experiment. His brother and eight others were killed. This disaster made Nobel try even harder to invent a safe explosive. A few years later, Nobel succeeded. He invented dynamite. Dynamite became widely used around the world. Nobel's discovery made him rich.

Later, Nobel invented a device that created **controversy**. The device could be used to kill. Yet, Nobel was committed to peace. When he died, he left money and directions for giving yearly awards for good works. The Nobel Prize is still given today in the areas of science, literature, and peace.

⚙ FLUENCY TIP

Change expressions to convey feelings about the tragedy described in the second paragraph and Nobel's positive contributions that follow.

Nobel Peace Prize Comprehension

Read each question. Darken the circle next to the correct answer.

1. What did Nobel do?

   Ⓐ built roads

   Ⓑ constructed buildings

   Ⓒ manufactured explosives

   Ⓓ taught science

2. How did the tragedy of his brother's death affect Nobel?

   Ⓐ It spurred him to find a safe explosive.

   Ⓑ It made him give up his experiments.

   Ⓒ It made him work for peace in the world.

   Ⓓ It made him want to find an explosive that could hurt others.

3. How did Nobel gain his fortune?

   Ⓐ He made a fortune selling dynamite.

   Ⓑ His father left it to him.

   Ⓒ The second device he invented sold well.

   Ⓓ People sent money to him to support his peace efforts.

4. What does the sentence below mean?
"Later, Nobel invented a device that created controversy."

   Ⓐ Nobel invented a new device that everyone wanted.

   Ⓑ No one liked Nobel's new invention.

   Ⓒ Nobel wanted peace, yet his invention could be used to kill.

   Ⓓ Nobel's new invention didn't do what it claimed to do.

Answer the question using complete sentences.

5. How do you know that Nobel was committed to peace?

_____

_____

_____

Jody Williams and the ICBL

5

In the early 1980s, Jody Williams was working in El Salvador. She was helping a | 20
group that provided aid and **artificial** limbs to children who had lost their limbs when | 35
land mines exploded. | 38

From a study by the International Red Cross, Williams discovered that 100 million | 51
land mines were buried throughout the world. Each year, about 26,000 people died when | 65
they stepped on one. Many times the land mines had been buried during a **previous** war. | 81
Unfortunately, they had never been dug up when the **dispute** ended, and the explosives | 95
could still explode. | 98

In 1991, Williams and others formed the International Campaign to Ban Landmines | 110
(ICBL). Their goals were to ban land mines worldwide and to establish a fund to pay for | 127
clearing existing land mines. | 131

By 1997, thirty countries had banned land mines. That year Williams and the ICBL | 145
were awarded the Nobel Peace Prize. Today, they continue to work to rid the world | 160
of land mines. | 163

 FLUENCY TIP

Think about the meaning of the piece and how to convey it. Vary the speed, volume, and intensity of your voice to meet the tone of the passage.

Jody Williams and the ICBL Comprehension

Read each question. Darken the circle next to the correct answer.

1. Why did people most likely bury land mines?

Ⓐ They did it during a war to stop the enemy from moving closer.

Ⓑ They did it during a war to prevent the inhabitants from leaving.

Ⓒ They did it before a war to define the country's borders.

Ⓓ They did it before the war to keep the inhabitants from farming.

2. Why did some children get hurt by land mines?

Ⓐ They were playing with land mines.

Ⓑ They played in an area where they knew land mines were buried.

Ⓒ Unknowingly, they played in an area where land mines were buried.

Ⓓ They were trying to dig up the land mines.

3. What does the ICBL do?

Ⓐ provide artificial limbs to children

Ⓑ pay to have land mines cleared

Ⓒ pay to bury land mines

Ⓓ see that people use land mines safely

4. In what year was the ICBL formed?

Ⓐ 1980

Ⓑ 1991

Ⓒ 1997

Ⓓ 2006

Answer the question using complete sentences.

5. Do you think Williams deserved the Nobel Peace Prize? Explain.

_____

_____

_____

Doctors Without Borders

	3

Doctors Without Borders (DWB) was founded in the early 1970s in France. It is an organization made up of doctors, nurses, and medical **administrators** who volunteer their services. DWB works to give aid around the world. The members help victims of natural disasters. They also provide aid during man-made disasters, like war.

Doctors Without Borders believes that national boundaries and political **disputes** do not **influence** who receives aid. DWB has succeeded in living up to its ideals. The organization has grown from a small group of French doctors to thousands of volunteers worldwide.

In 1999 Doctors Without Borders was awarded the Nobel Peace Prize. The organization received about one million dollars. DWB decided to use the award to distribute lifesaving medicines. These medicines would fight illnesses that kill people in developing countries.

18
29
43
55
65
80
94
96
108
121
131
135

⚙️ FLUENCY TIP

Think about the positive contribution this organization is making. Use expression and stress key words to convey that enthusiasm to your listeners.

118

Doctors Without Borders Comprehension

Read each question. Darken the circle next to the correct answer.

1. What do participants in Doctors Without Borders have in common?

Ⓐ They all are doctors.

Ⓑ They all received the Nobel Peace Prize over the years.

Ⓒ They all are from developing countries.

Ⓓ They all work in the medical profession.

2. What does the name of the organization suggest?

Ⓐ The members go to any country where there is a need for aid.

Ⓑ The members are from one nation.

Ⓒ The members wear clothes with borders on the hems.

Ⓓ The members work on the borders of their countries only.

3. Who started the organization?

Ⓐ people in the United States

Ⓑ people in France

Ⓒ people in a war zone

Ⓓ people who liked to travel to developing countries

4. How did Doctors Without Borders use the prize money?

Ⓐ to pay the workers

Ⓑ to build a headquarters for the organization

Ⓒ to buy lifesaving medicines to be used in developing countries

Ⓓ to buy equipment to be used when giving aid

Answer the question using complete sentences.

5. Do you think Doctors Without Borders deserved the Nobel Peace Prize? Explain.

_____

_____

_____

Lesson 15: Spectacular Science
Connecting Background

Theme Notes

We continue to understand more about the world around us because scientists identify a need or a process to do something in a different way. They experiment to prove these ideas. The readings in this lesson focus on three of these scientists and their contributions in the medical field—Daniel Hale Williams, Gertrude B. Elion, and Ben Carson.

Fluency Focus: Expression

To be fluent readers, people need to read with expression. This is important because it makes reading more interesting and can help improve understanding. Readers can use their voice to stress certain words or phrases. Often, punctuation will help the reader read with expression. However, sometimes readers have to decide how to read with expression on their own, based on the purpose of the sentence.

Fluency Practice

Write these sentences on the board: *My experiment was a huge success! Would you like to see what I invented?*

Encourage students to read the sentences with the proper expression.

Comprehension Focus: Sequence

Biographies tell about a person's life. The events are often recounted in sequence. Sequence is the order in which events happen. Clue words can help a reader understand the sequence of life events. Words such as *first*, *next*, *last*, and *finally* tell about sequence. Dates are also clues that tell time sequence. The Sequence Chain on page 121 can help students understand the order of events in each biography.

VOCABULARY

- *Daniel Hale Williams*
  enrolled
  surgery
  patient

- *Gertrude B. Elion*
  experimental
  synthesized
  patents

- *Ben Carson*
  internship
  residency
  determination

Connecting Reading 7–8, SV 9781419036453

Sequence Chain

Title _____

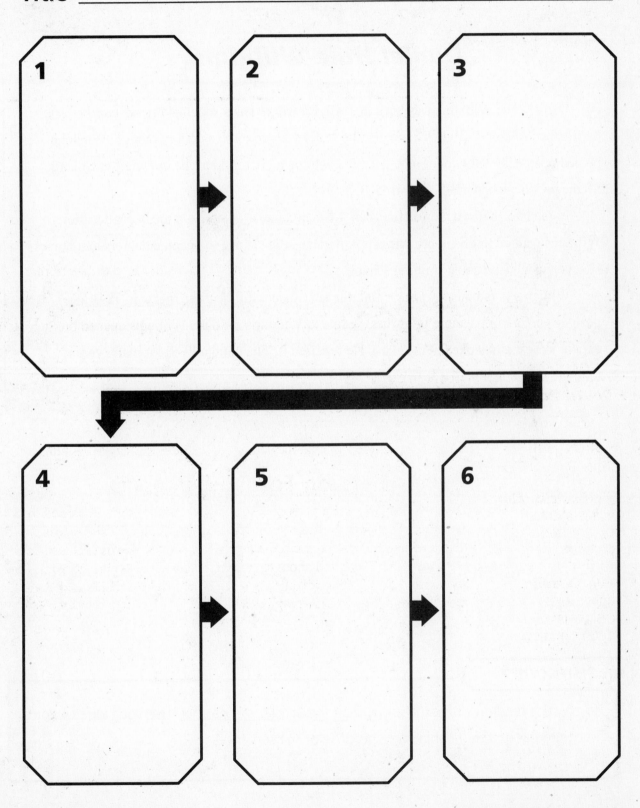

Daniel Hale Williams

	3

Daniel Hale Williams was born in 1856. He worked as a shoemaker and a barber after | 19

he finished school. Williams knew that he really wanted to be a doctor, though. When he | 35

helped people, he felt good. So he got a job helping a doctor. Later he **enrolled** in Chicago | 53

Medical College and graduated in 1883. | 59

In the late 1800s, it was difficult for African Americans to get a medical education. | 74

Williams wanted to give more African Americans the chance to become doctors and nurses. | 88

He opened a hospital and training school. | 95

Williams is famous for performing the first successful heart **surgery**. In 1893 a | 108

patient with a knife wound to his heart came to Williams for help. Williams opened the | 124

patient's chest and looked at the heart. He repaired it. The patient lived for many years | 140

following the surgery. | 143

⚙ FLUENCY TIP

To practice reading with expression, read the article to a partner. Use your tone of voice to communicate the meaning and purpose of the sentences.

Daniel Hale Williams Comprehension

Read each question. Darken the circle next to the correct answer.

1. What did Williams do before assisting a doctor?

Ⓐ He made shoes.

Ⓑ He went to medical school.

Ⓒ He opened a hospital.

Ⓓ He trained nurses.

2. Why did Williams open a training school?

Ⓐ to teach people how to cut hair

Ⓑ to show how he did surgeries

Ⓒ to help African Americans get medical care

Ⓓ to teach African Americans to be doctors and nurses

3. For what procedure is Williams best known?

Ⓐ heart surgery

Ⓑ brain surgery

Ⓒ lung surgery

Ⓓ eye surgery

4. What can you conclude about Williams?

Ⓐ He was not a good surgeon.

Ⓑ He was a caring doctor.

Ⓒ He worked long hours.

Ⓓ He made lots of money.

Answer the question using complete sentences.

5. Why was Williams's surgery described in the article considered spectacular?

_____

_____

_____

Lesson 15: Spectacular Science
Connecting Reading 7–8, SV 9781419036453

Gertrude B. Elion

3

Growing up in New York, Gertrude Elion had a thirst for knowledge. She attended   17
Hunter College, where she decided to major in chemistry. When her grandfather died of   31
cancer, she decided to one day find a cure.   40

In 1941 Elion earned a master's degree in chemistry. After working in a few   54
laboratories, she became an assistant to George Hitchings. He encouraged Elion in her   67
quest for knowledge.   70

Elion became head of the Department of **Experimental** Therapy at that same lab.   83
By 1949 she had accomplished part of her goal. She had **synthesized** a medicine that   98
was used to treat leukemia, a form of cancer. In 1988, Elion received the Nobel Prize in   115
medicine. Elion died in 1999. In her lifetime, Elion was granted 45 **patents**.   128

⚙ FLUENCY TIP

Preview the pronunciation of words in bold type so you can pronounce them correctly
and read them fluently. This will help you read with better expression.

Name _____   Date _____

Gertrude B. Elion Comprehension

Read each question. Darken the circle next to the correct answer.

1. What does the article mean when it says, "Elion had a thirst for knowledge"?

   Ⓐ Elion drank a lot of liquids.

   Ⓑ Elion didn't know much.

   Ⓒ Elion had the highest grades in her school.

   Ⓓ Elion liked to learn.

2. What happened when Elion's grandfather died?

   Ⓐ Elion earned her master's degree.

   Ⓑ Elion decided to find a cancer cure.

   Ⓒ Elion began working with George Hitchings.

   Ⓓ Elion got her first patent.

3. What can you infer from the article?

   Ⓐ Elion experimented to find a cancer cure.

   Ⓑ Other scientists did not like to work for Elion.

   Ⓒ Elion found a cure for cancer.

   Ⓓ Elion died of cancer.

4. How was George Hitchings a mentor to Elion?

   Ⓐ He hired Elion as the department head of a lab.

   Ⓑ His cancer research lead to Elion's interest in cancer medicines.

   Ⓒ He encouraged Elion to continue to research new ideas.

   Ⓓ He was one of Elion's professors in college.

Answer the question using complete sentences.

5. What event in your life has influenced the way you think or act?

   _____

   _____

   _____

Lesson 15: Spectacular Science
Connecting Reading 7–8, SV 9781419036453

Ben Carson

	2

As a child, Benjamin Carson lived with his mother and brother in a poor neighborhood   17
in Detroit, Michigan. The boys fell behind in school, and by the fifth grade, Ben was at the   35
bottom of his class. His classmates called him "dummy," and he had very low self-esteem.   50

When Mrs. Carson saw her sons' failing grades, she decided to turn their lives around.   65
She limited their television viewing and refused to let them play until they finished their   80
homework. She required that they read two library books every week and do a written   95
report on each book.   99

Carson developed a hunger for knowledge and decided to become a physician. After   112
graduating from Yale University, he studied medicine at the University of Michigan. There   125
he developed an interest in surgery. Carson completed his **internship** and **residency** at   138
Johns Hopkins Hospital. At age 32, he became the Director of Pediatric Neurosurgery at   152
Johns Hopkins Hospital.   155

In 1987 Carson made medical history when he separated twins joined at the head.   169
After the 22-hour operation, the twins were able to live independently. Through hard work   183
and **determination**, Ben Carson has become an American hero.   192

⚙ FLUENCY TIP

Read this selection in a manner that shows you are sharing interesting information.

Connecting Reading 7–8, SV 9781419036453

Ben Carson Comprehension

Read each question. Darken the circle next to the correct answer.

1. What made Mrs. Carson change her sons' study habits?

Ⓐ Both boys were doing poorly in school.

Ⓑ The boys spent all their time watching TV.

Ⓒ They were getting into trouble in the community.

Ⓓ Classmates called Ben Carson a dummy.

2. When did Carson develop an interest in surgery?

Ⓐ when he read a book about medicine while in high school

Ⓑ when he saw a television show about surgeons

Ⓒ at Yale University

Ⓓ while studying medicine at the University of Michigan

3. Who were Carson's patients?

Ⓐ children

Ⓑ older people

Ⓒ men

Ⓓ women

4. What is Carson best known for?

Ⓐ performing long operations

Ⓑ going to Yale University

Ⓒ separating twins joined at the head

Ⓓ being the youngest director at a hospital

Answer the questions using complete sentences.

5. If you limited your TV viewing and read two books a week, would you do better in school? Why or why not?

_____

_____

_____

Answer Key

Page 11
1. C 2. B 3. A 4. B
5. Answers will vary.

Page 13
1. B 2. B 3. A 4. A
5. Answers will vary.

Page 15
1. C 2. A 3. D 4. D
5. Answers will vary.

Page 19
1. A 2. C 3. D 4. C
5. Answers will vary.

Page 21
1. C 2. A 3. A 4. C
5. Answers will vary.

Page 23
1. B 2. C 3. B 4. C
5. Answers will vary.

Page 27
1. B 2. A 3. A 4. C
5. Answers will vary.

Page 29
1. A 2. C 3. B 4. D
5. Drawings will vary but should show dots of light for stars.

Page 31
1. B 2. A 3. D 4. A
5. Answers will vary.

Page 35
1. D 2. B 3. A 4. C
5. Answers will vary.

Page 37
1. B 2. A 3. B 4. A
5. Binns is a hero because he made a radio call and saved many people even though he was in great danger.

Page 39
1. D 2. A 3. C 4. D
5. Possible answer: People did not understand the technology of radio waves, so they did not think it would work.

Page 43
1. B 2. A 3. C 4. B
5. Answers will vary.

Page 45
1. A 2. D 3. B 4. D
5. Answers will vary.

Page 47
1. C 2. D 3. B 4. A
5. Answers will vary.

Page 51
1. A 2. C 3. B 4. C
5. Possible answer: They depend more on their senses of hearing and touch.

Page 53
1. B 2. B 3. D 4. C
5. Possible answer: They can live a more independent life because they can read information written in Braille through books or other Braille printed materials.

Page 55
1. B 2. A 3. B 4. A
5. Most likely answer: Glaucoma is the most severe disease because it must be treated for the rest of one's life.

Page 59
1. D 2. D 3. B 4. A
5. Possible answer: The organs would weaken and eventually stop working.

Page 61
1. A 2. C 3. B 4. C
5. The nutrients are absorbed by blood that travels near the digestive organs.

Page 63
1. C 2. B 3. D 4. B
5. Possible answer: Your body would not sense things that are dangerous, so your body might get hurt in that area.

Page 67
1. C 2. B 3. A 4. D
5. Possible answer: Wear bug spray and cover the body with clothing, including long pants and shirts with long sleeves.

Page 69
1. B 2. A 3. A 4. B
5. Possible answer: People are afraid that if the microbe gets out, it will cause a mass outbreak and kill many people.

Page 71
1. B 2. C 3. C 4. B
5. Possible answer: More people were getting vaccines to prevent the disease.

Page 75
1. D 2. A 3. C 4. B
5. Answers will vary.

Page 77
1. C 2. A 3. A 4. D
5. Answers will vary.

Page 79
1. C 2. B 3. C 4. A
5. Answers will vary.

Page 83
1. B 2. A 3. D 4. C
5. Answers will vary.

Page 85
1. D 2. A 3. B 4. A
5. Answers will vary.

Page 87
1. B 2. B 3. C 4. C
5. Answers will vary.

Page 91
1. A 2. C 3. A 4. B
5. Answers will vary.

Page 93
1. A 2. A 3. C 4. C
5. Answers will vary.

Page 95
1. B 2. A 3. D 4. C
5. Answers will vary.

Page 99
1. C 2. B 3. A 4. D
5. Answers will vary.

Page 101
1. C 2. A 3. A 4. A
5. Answers will vary.

Page 103
1. D 2. A 3. B 4. C
5. Answers will vary.

Page 107
1. A 2. D 3. D 4. C
5. Answers will vary.

Page 109
1. C 2. C 3. A 4. A
5. Answers will vary.

Page 111
1. D 2. D 3. C 4. B
5. Answers will vary.

Page 115
1. C 2. A 3. A 4. C
5. Possible answer: He left instructions for awarding financial prizes to people who worked for peace.

Page 117
1. A 2. C 3. B 4. B
5. Most likely answer: Williams worked to ban a deadly weapon that could hurt many people.

Page 119
1. D 2. A 3. B 4. C
5. Most likely answer: The DWB worked to improve the lives of many who would not ordinarily get medical assistance.

Page 123
1. A 2. D 3. A 4. B
5. It was the first open-heart surgery, and the person lived for many years after it.

Page 125
1. D 2. B 3. A 4. C
5. Answers will vary.

Page 127
1. A 2. D 3. A 4. C
5. Answers will vary.

Answer Key
Connecting Reading 7–8, SV 9781419036453